Wings
for our
Children

Essentials of Becoming a Play Therapist

GSPH

Gregory P. Lubimiv

Published by

GENERAL STORE
PUBLISHING HOUSE

1 Main Street Burnstown, Ontario, Canada K0J 1G0
Telephone (613) 432-7697 or (613) 432-9385

ISBN 0-919431-84-4
Printed and Bound in Canada.

Cover Design and Layout by Leanne Enright

Copyright © 1994
The General Store Publishing House
Burnstown, Ontario, Canada

Canadian Cataloguing in Publication Data

Lubimiv, Gregory
    Wings for our children: essentials of becoming a play therapist

Includes bibliographical references
ISBN 0-919431-84-4

    1. Play therapy.   I. Title.
RJ505.P6L82 1994   618.92'891653   C94-900203-8

First Printing May 1994
Second Printing March 1996

Over my years as a practitioner, many people have influenced me in both subtle and dramatic ways. I would like to acknowledge these special people and thank them for their caring and willingness to share their wisdom.

First, I would like to thank my friend, teacher and colleague, Joyce Cohen. It was through Joyce that I first became introduced to the field of play therapy and it was through her modelling that I found myself able to be both open to and critical of new learning.

Second, though I have never had any personal contact, I have found three pioneers in the field of play and clinical psychotherapy have had tremendous influence on me. Jean Piaget, whose theories of Child Development and Play are both enlightening and useful. Virginia Axline, whose work and writings demostrated clearly the power of play therapy, and Milton Erikson, who was able to be so creative and adapt his therapy to the specific needs of each patient.

Third, thank you to all the children I have worked with in play therapy. These special people shared with me their pain, their joy and their love. You made my work both interesting and enjoyable — and each of you added something to my own growth as a person as well as a therapist.

Finally, and most importantly, thanks and a great big hug to Julie; my wife, my friend and my colleague. Julie gave me the opportunity to begin this book and without her consistent support and enthusiasm would have been far from being completed.

Dedication

I would like to dedicate this book to my children,
Aaron, Natasha, Nikolas, Julien and Layna
who helped the child in me grow and feel accepted and loved.

"There are only two lasting bequests we can hope to give our children. One of these is roots; the other wings."

Hodding Carter

Contents

Foreword

In my experience as a therapist, I have found play therapy to be the most exciting, interesting and challenging medium in my clinical practice. As well, I believe that play therapy and play generally have been the most important factors in my own personal and professional growth. There are several reasons for this:

1. This form of therapy demands flexibility, creativity and spontaneity. These attributes are the basic ingredients necessary to tap your existing and potential resources within.

2. Play therapy is fun. As one of the great sports figures stated several years ago, "It's incredible I am paid to do what I enjoy most." Working with children through play allows us to unleash the child inside each of us. That child, with its curiosity, playfulness and creativity can lead us to new knowledge and experiences in every session.

3. Play therapy is effective. What better reward is there in our practice than to see children we work with become healthier and better able to cope with the stresses and strains of everyday life? Once we become attuned to the various signs and symbols, we can recognize change in a child between and even within sessions.

My goal in this book is to stimulate readers to become at ease with the power of play and to move towards harnessing that power in their clinical work. I hope many will decide to continue their study to become play therapists in the formal sense.

The content of this book and its viewpoint on play are of course full of my own biases which arise from my particular subjective realities (and fantasies). In accepting this, the reader must also accept that as your competence grows so will your own biases. I hope that in your own development one of your biases will be to remain open to new experiences and influences which will in turn push you forward to new frontiers.

I would also like to note that the field of play and play therapy is so large and diverse that it is impossible to provide a full picture of the theories, models and techniques. In fact, I will purposely focus only briefly on the formal theories. Rather, I would like to provide a view of my perspectives on this form of therapy and concentrate on the practical frameworks which will be helpful to the beginner.

Your view and understanding of play and play therapy will distinguish you as being either a play therapist or a therapist who utilizes play. There is a clear distinction between the two, but they are often blurred. This does not mean that one is better or worse than the other - they are just different. For example, I do know a little about cars and will change the oil, put in a new radiator or fix a flat tire - but I cannot claim to be a mechanic, nor do I wish to.

Understanding and utilizing play is not only for work with children, although this will be the prime focus of this book. It is also extremely powerful with adolescents, adults, families, groups and organizations. The context, the presentation and the content may change to varying degrees; however, your play and playfulness can truly be universal.

I hope the reader will see this book as only one stepping stone across a wide river. To get across, then, you must not remain on the one stone, but move to other stones which seem strong enough to support you and high enough to keep you dry.

Do not be afraid to get your feet wet; make a game of crossing, enjoying the challenge and anticipating the results.

I look forward to sharing a stone with you and, sometime in the future, meeting you on the other side.

Importance Of Play

The first step and necessary foundation of being a play therapist is to have an understanding and acceptance of the importance and the power of play.

For centuries now, it has been quite clear that there is a common element among all children in the world — play. No matter what their sex, religion or culture, children engage themselves and/or each other in often aimless and illogical flights of fancy which are labelled "play". Serious observers, however, recognize that there is a ritual character in much play and that children can be engaged to learn through play.

Plato is often cited as the first to recognize the practical value of play "from his prescription in the laws to distribute apples among boys to help them learn arithmetic, and to give real miniature tools to those three-year-olds who were later to become builders." (Millar, 1977, p 13.)

Over the last two centuries, a number of theories have been developed to explain the connection between play and human development. These include the ideas of Charles Darwin, Sigmund Freud, Eric Erikson and Jean Piaget. Although each gives a different explanation of the *raison d'etre*, they all conclude that play is, in fact, necessary for child development.

In more recent times play has received even more attention for its apparent healing power and the field's pioneers were quick to take note and develop methods to utilize play therapeutically. Virginia Axline noted that, "Play therapy is based upon the fact that play is the child's natural medium of self-expression." (Axline, 1947, p 9.)

It is now quite accepted that the function of play is adaptive, helping a child assimilate experiences and gain mastery over reality and unpleasant experiences. By observing a child's play, it is therefore possible to gain information about that child's emotional and social development. It has been noted that all children play, but children experiencing a disturbance exhibit distinctive characteristics. "It is not the content of play which differs from that of ordinary children, but its structure, style and cohesion." (Millar, 1977, p 236.)

Therefore, you may have two children playing with blocks, building and knocking them down, but one child is labelled "healthy" and the other "disturbed". There is no one action which does this . . . it may be the intensity of play, the inability to shift to a new activity, regressing in age, or any number of behaviours. "A frustrating experience, even if only temporary, has been shown to make children play less constructively and at a more immature level." (Millar, 1977, p 237.)

It is clear then that play is the child's medium for moving through life and achieving his full self. "In every child is a thrust to actualize his or her potential. Potential is always there and is hungry for expression." (Snyder, Snyder, Snyder, 1980, p 22.)

When a child faces barriers he cannot overcome, his play attempts to resolve the conflict and so becomes symbolic of the conflict. "Manifest behaviours give us a view of children's perceptions of themselves." (Samuels, 1977, p 15.) What then is children's perception of themselves in their world when they continually break toys or when they sit silently in a corner playing with their fingers? Again, the exact message is not identical for each child . . . except in that it is clear that the child is stuck and needs help to move beyond where he is. This is where play therapy comes in . . . "The play therapy room where the child is the most important person, where he is in command . . . he suddenly feels that here he can unfold his wings . . . " (Axline, 1947, p 16.)

The other important factor for all children is that they need relationships which provide them with confirmation that they are all right. "Children want to be in a relationship with the significant adults in their world as well as with their peers. Children are miserable when they feel out of a relationship. Then they are apt to resort to odd behaviour patterns that do not work, such as attacking, crying or withdrawing." (Snyder, Snyder, Snyder, 1980, p 25.) Unfortunately, many children face a lack of acceptance and a vacuum of supportive relationships. This is why the relationship between the child and the therapist can be so intense and also so subject to transference/counter-transference.

Core Knowledge Base

I believe that there are several pre-requisites to becoming an effective play therapist. These are my views and are derived from my own experiences as a therapist and as a trainer:

1. Child Development
2. Child Management and Parenting
3. Systems
4. Triangulation
5. Transference/Counter-Transference
6. Hypothesis-Building
7. Termination Process

You will have noticed that techniques are not a part of this list. That is because I do not see them as a pre-requisite of play therapy. You will find that if you have your foundation firm, techniques will fall into place quickly and you will be able to learn, adapt and create new "tools" easily in accordance with your individual personality, interests and skills.

BEING A CHILD

I don't believe everyone can become a good play therapist. There must be something special inside each of us to be able to "play" well. Many people can play the violin but only a few stand out as "virtuosos". Why is this? Master violinists have several characteristics in common, but there is one feature which stands out clearly. They all speak about their music and their instrument as being a part of their being. As Magic Johnson once said about his basketball, "The ball is an extension of me."

Play therapy (or anything we wish to do well) must be an extension of yourself. Since play therapy calls for play and humour and fun, that part of you which we often refer to as the child must be free to introduce itself into the session and be with the child in need.

All of us were at one time children; all of us still have that child within us. That child leads us to make irrational decisions or pushes us to pull a practical joke on a family member or friend.

You must become comfortable with letting that child come out and run freely. We can recognize the child inside of us because of its special qualities, which include:

1. Energy and vitality
2. Curiosity
3. Excitement
4. Creativity
5. Trust
6. Inventiveness
7. Adaptability

It is these qualities which will draw a child to you and vice versa. Of course, to do this you must also like children. If you don't, then it is best not to pursue work with this age group.

One of the common barriers potential play therapists face is the fear of "looking silly" to others. You must shake this if you want to pursue this form of therapy. I often felt a little embarrassed when I first began to practise play therapy and would make sure I was not too loud when pretending to be Superman and I'd get up quickly from the floor if someone opened the door to the play room. I have now passed this stage and am able to shut out the external world and focus solely on the world the child creates in the session.

The child in you, like all children, needs nurturing, support and stimulation. The best way to get these is from other children, in play which has no purpose other than having a good time.

Go to a playground or school yard and watch children playing. Play at the sand table, draw or make a space ship out of Lego. Watch cartoons and read story books. Hang around your children, or nieces and nephews, to learn what they like and dislike. Go back to your old neighbourhood or school and revisit your memories as a child. For some this may be a painful process, but it can help deal with another barrier that effects a number of therapists, which we will investigate further in the Transference/Counter-Transference section.

Volunteer to be Santa at Christmas, the Easter Bunny at Easter or The Great Pumpkin at Halloween. Volunteer to do role playing at workshops you may attend. Be a clown at a children's party or play a favourite musical instrument. Join the local drama club and try out acting, and so on. Once you begin to look for ways to stimulate the child in you, you will soon find there are opportunities all around you.

One of my hobbies, which has been extremely helpful in my work with children (and adults), is magic. As an amateur magician, I take every available opportunity to give a children's show where I can entertain and have fun with them. Each of us has a talent or talents which can be brought to play in our work with children and can help to stimulate the child inside. Singing, dancing, drawing, origami, playing a musical instrument, making crafts, acting, are all potential play therapy tools and should not be overlooked.

Summary

If you accept the importance of play in child development and the "magic" of play as a therapeutic tool, you should reinforce your knowledge base in the core area. In addition, you need to get in touch with the child. This is your rite of passage in becoming an effective play therapist. The easy part is to find the models, approaches, and techniques that fit your style and personality and then, as Beethoven might have said, "Play for all you are worth".

Child Development

Understanding the nature and processes of normal child development is essential to working with children and families. The therapist needs to be aware of the various stages children pass through in their maturation process. As well, he needs to understand what to expect from children at different ages in determining how to act or react.

Generally speaking, there are two forces at work in determining a child's development; these come under the headings of biological and environmental forces. Although these have been well studied and researched, there is still a debate as to which has more or less influence. However, there is no debate that children do go through fairly predictable, consistent stages. We know that a child crawls at about six months and walks at about one year of age. We are not concerned about a child who cannot read at age three but would be if the child was eight or nine.

There are a number of theoretical frameworks which help us to understand and translate the processes that children go through, including those developed by Erik Erikson (1950), Margaret Mahler (1975), Jean Piaget (1969) and Anna Freud (1965).

In order to assess the relevance of developmental patterns the therapist needs to be able to focus on a number of areas. These include:

    a. The physical status of the child. What is the child capable of doing or not doing physically?

    b. The mood or emotional tone of the child. What affect does the child display, how does he show his feelings? Are the feelings revealed appropriate?

    c. The social relationships the child has with others. Are these appropriate? How strong are they? Are they easily influenced?

    d. The ability of the child to conceptualize, abstract and generalize information.

e. The ability of the child to communicate any or all of the above. Can the child understand what you are saying? Can he effectively get across what he wishes to say to others?

In spite of our knowledge of predictable patterns and stages that children go through, one must be careful not to oversimplify this to the point of equating a particular age and behavior with a specific factor. For example, three ten year old boys are very close friends. One of the boys moves to another part of the country and leaves his friends behind. One of the friends reacts by being very sad and withdrawn, while the other begins to exhibit a great deal of anger and aggression with his family and other children. Despite the very different reactions both boys are having a "normal" response. In another example, a young girl becomes angry with her teacher and is very sullen and quiet. Later, she is angry with her mother and stamps her feet, yelling and shouting at her parent, while even later she is angry with her friend and throws a ball at her.

What we need to remember is that there are multi-determinants of behaviour and multiple lines of development. (Greenspan, 1975.)

Knowledge of child development becomes crucial in play therapy as it helps to direct your work in so many ways, determining the words you use, what toys you use, how long your stories are, to fit the child's development stage. Is the child's thumb-sucking a problem? Is the sudden verbal challenging of a parent by a twelve-year-old unusual and abnormal? How should a four-year-old react when their mother leaves the room on the first visit? How should an eight-year-old react? Why might they be reacting in this way? There are a thousand questions and often no real right answer. However, a tremendous amount of direction and guidance can be gained by knowing what is "normal".

I recall an experience recently when a therapist had a child draw in a play session. He was asked to draw himself and his family. The result was a picture made up of a circle with two eyes, a mouth, a nose and two ears. There were no arms, hands, legs or feet. The therapist remembered in a previous consultation that this suggested a difficulty in making contact with people and a sense of being stuck or frozen. I was asked to confirm this suspicion. However, when I became aware that the child was only three, the only remark I could make was, "That's a pretty good drawing for a three-year-old." The therapist, in his enthusiasm to use this tool, had forgotten that the previous client was eight years old.

I urge the reader to look at the various resources related to child development and the maturation process. Spend time with children, observe them in the playground, notice the differences in ages. When you see children's drawings, guess their age, and check to see how accurate you are.

By understanding what is normal behaviour, affect and thinking of children, you will better be able to understand and deal with what is considered abnormal or problematic behaviour. As well, you will be able to keep problems in perspective for yourself, the parent(s) and other concerned adults.

There is a balancing act for all of us to accomplish in working with children and families. How do we keep from making a mountain out of a mole hill — while ensuring we don't make mole hills out of mountains? Having a strong background in Child Development will not guarantee this will never happen — but you will certainly be better prepared.

Child Management

In my experience of training clinicians, one weakness which presents itself constantly is in the area of child management and parenting training and skills. This is often compounded by the fact that many clinicians are not parents themselves. This, of course, should not prevent anyone from doing excellent work with children, but it is a handicap to overcome. Good child management skills, like most things in life, come from healthy experience and practice. Having children can provide a practitioner with a fertile field of experience to draw from. On the down side, therapists who have their own children may also be more at risk of counter-transference or of being more rigid in their approaches and perspectives.

For clinicians without children, (as I was for many years), it is necessary to expose yourself to young people as much as possible, observing and participating with children in their own activities.

Also, we must not forget one of our richest resources is our own selves; we were all children once.

In order to work well with disturbed children, one should be able to identify "normal" behaviour. Awareness of this can prevent "much ado about nothing." This calls for knowledge of child management.

In addition, because of the wide range of dysfunctional behaviours we will see and experience, it is crucial to know how to react, to manage, to re-direct those behaviours as necessary. As I use some limit-setting in my therapy, child management is even more important than if I was a non-directive therapist. Therefore, I need to know about natural, logical consequences and about the child's physical, emotional and intellectual abilities.

Familiarity with child management also helps me to prepare for a common occurrence in therapy and a paradoxical bind which can make therapy impotent. That is, the phenomenon of the child's behaviour becoming worse before becoming better. Knowing that this is likely to happen, I am able to predict it for the parents, teacher (if appropriate), and for myself. In my first few years of therapy, I was often thrown off by a parent pulling a child out of therapy, or a principal suspending a child from school, and deciding therapy was a waste of time. Now I am able to discuss this with the people in the child's life and, to reframe the increase in disturbance as a positive sign, I will state, "This means that we are getting somewhere and change is occurring." I am often disconcerted at how often therapy is abandoned (sometimes by the therapist), because of an incorrect interpretation of the child's intensification of behaviours.

Child management and parenting skills also allow for a better connection with the parents making them allies in the therapy. Being able to give concrete suggestions for handling behaviour, or being able to reframe or help parents understand behaviour better, can make the difference between success and failure.

For example, a three-year-old girl was referred to me whose mother was very concerned that her daughter had started to stutter. The doctor had given a medical opinion that there was nothing physically wrong with the child. My response to the mother was not to initiate play therapy, but to explain to her that it was a common experience (normalization) for many young children to go through a short period of stuttering, (especially between ages three to five), as their vocabulary, ability to speak/pronounce, and conceptual/intellectual skills are often moving at different speeds. I then gave her some suggestions of how to react to the stuttering, (no pressure, allowing time for the child, not finishing the sentence for her, etc.). I asked the mother to check back with me the next month to see if there was any need for further assessment/investigation. About six weeks later, I called her as I had not heard anything. She apologized for forgetting to call me and said her daughter seemed much better now, and it was more her worry which had been the problem.

There are many books, brochures, workshops, video/audio tapes available on the topic of parenting and child management. A number of these are listed in the reference section.

Ensure that you become aware of the different needs of children in this area as they grow. Child management with a four-year-old is really quite different than with a fifteen-year-old. There may also be some cultural variables you may need to consider. This is where your knowledge of child development will be especially useful.

The essence of effective parenting and child management skills also provides a solid base for creating a safe, healthy and nurturing environment for children to grow up in. Whether at home, at school or in a therapy room, there are ingredients necessary to ensure a child has the best opportunity to "become".

These ingredients include:
1. Unconditional Love/Acceptance
2. Predictability
3. Consistency
4. Safety
5. Belonging

In Play Therapy, I try to ensure that each child is guaranteed the ingredients, at least during their time with me. For example, I schedule sessions for the same time, day and place (Predictability). Although this may not be possible from time to time, it should be the exception not the rule. One of the rules I always set with the child is that neither of us are allowed to hurt each other (Safety).

Each therapist has a different style in working with children and may incorporate any of a number of models/techniques. You may be directive or non-directive, behavioural or emotional, psycho-analytic or existential. To me, the important task at the initiation of therapy is to clarify the rules and expectations of yourself and the child and the consequences (if any) for breaking these. Also, I would mention, that whatever rules we set are for both of us. I have had to sit in a "time out chair" several times for forgetting a rule.

Common rules to consider are:
1. No hurting each other.
2. No leaving the room once the session starts.
3. Clean up in the last five minutes.
4. No taking play toys out of the room.
5. No damaging/breaking things on purpose.

Good child management also dictates that if rules are to be meaningful, consequences must be also set and applied where necessary.

I usually negotiate consequences with the child and the, majority of times, end up with a form of time out. For very young children, I use a timer with a buzzer which will go off after a set time (two or three minutes is a long time for a three year old).

I always make sure the child is aware of what rule was broken, what the agreed consequence was and how they feel about the process. Some therapists have chosen, for very disturbing behaviour, to use early termination of a session as a consequence. My preference is not to do this as you may inadvertently encourage a child to misbehave when they do not want to be in the room.

In effect, what I am suggesting is that to be an effective therapist you must also have the ingredients of an effective parent (at least for the time you are in session). As mentioned previously, there is a multitude of excellent books, articles, journals, etc., on parenting and child management. Take the time to read these to reflect on how you use these skills in your work.

Systems

Systems theory revolves around the concept of relationships and the interconnection between them. A system can be a family, a couple, a team, a company, a political party. Each of these systems seeks to survive and does so through constant sets of actions and reactions, labelled as inputs and outputs. Systems, as well, do not exist in isolation, and so we need to consider those other systems which interact with or influence them.

The family is one of the best known and accepted systems. Over the last three decades, systems theory has become a core model for work with children and adults through family therapy. "The family as a human institution is universal and has survived through history as the most workable kind of living unit for mediating the culture in preparing the young for the next generation." (Framo, 1982, p 4.)

Through study and observation a number of findings were made about family systems; many are relevant for other types of systems as well:

1. When the family is observed as an interacting unit it is learned that the family is an intricate system with its own bondings, rules, myths, regressive features and dynamic influences from previous generations. Intimates can drive each other crazy; problems are similar from one generation to the next, and adults use their spouses and children to live through inner conflicts derived from their families of origin.

2. The psychopathology that seems to exist only in the identified patient is found to be present, subliminally at least, in all family members and to be projected onto a scapegoat who cooperates with this role assignment and becomes the symptom bearer of a family-wide disturbance. Parts of the family pathology are found to be present in each member, like separate segments of a multi-layered jigsaw puzzle.

3. Seen in the context of the family, heretofore incomprehensible symptoms of the patient become decoded and make sense. (That is, the child who refuses to go to school, diagnosed as having "school phobia", has to stay home with his depressed mother because he is afraid she is going to kill herself; he was also delegated to send messages to the absent father).

4. As the symptoms of the identified patient diminish, someone else in the family develops symptoms. Psychopathology, seen previously as solely the outcome of internalized, insoluble intrapsychic conflicts, could balance family forces as well.

5. The psychology of intimate relationships is very different from that of all other social relationships. (You are a different person when you are with your family than you are with other people.)

6. Characteristics of individuals are peculiar to their context or system and can best be explained by analyzing the system, not just the individual.

7. In general systems theory, all systems are characterized by homeostasis, feedback loops, complementarity, and equifinality (tending toward a steady state). Family systems move toward diminishing or modifying personal change in relating to other family members. That is, the system resists individual efforts to change; it prescribes the member's behaviours to adapt to the need of the system. Anyone who tries to change his or her role in a family will soon find out what this means.

8. Interlocking, multi-person motivational systems, whereby one person carries part of the motivations and psychology of another, are only beginning to be understood. Wherever two or more persons are in close relationship they collusively carry psychic functions for each other. The collusion can be benign: If you are scared, I can afford to be brave; if you are responsible, I can allow myself to be irresponsible; if you take the hard line, I can take the soft line. The collusion can be more serious and unconscious: I will be your bad self and act out your impulses if you will never leave me.

9. Symptoms are formed, selected, faked, exchanged, maintained and reduced as a function of the relationship context in which they are embedded. (Framo, 1970, p 6.)

Systems, especially family systems, though resistant to change are constantly undergoing changes. As well, each of us belongs to several systems which are inter-connected. For example, a woman is part of the family system, a marital system, a member of her team at work, a member of the local women's association, etc. "While it is assumed that all people are members of different systems simultaneously, they do not maintain the same allegiance to each system. There are varying degrees of relative importance which the different systems occupy in a given person's life. The most important system is assumed to be the family system because this is the place where the individual learns to interact". (Koman/Stechier, p 7.)

Each family is a unique system which will develop and respond to internal and external environments in its own fashion. As the family is called on to respond to a change, the members will act, react and move along at their own pace. "A family's pace at any given moment may vary. Different stages will be handled differently by different families. For instance, one family may adjust quite easily to the birth of children but have extreme difficulty when it is time for these same children to go to college, whereas another family may have had difficulty in adjusting to the presence of adolescents in their family but moves rapidly through the phase of launching children into their own lives. It is also possible for a system to become 'stuck' at any time, but these times usually occur around a point of transition from one stage to another". (Koman/Stechier, p 7.)

The more vulnerable a system feels to change, the more rigid and resistant it becomes. "The greater the system's need for stability, the greater the severity and irreversibility of the resulting pathology. In other words, the system reorganized itself so that it will not have to change . . . To counteract the stress inherent in developmental change, the system substitutes the stress evoked by the symptomatic behaviour of one family member, the identified patient, around which the anxieties of all family members revolve." (Andolfi/Angelo/Menghi/Nicolo-Corigliano, 1983, p 18.)

What does all this mean for the person working with children in play therapy, or any form of therapy?

If you are "stuck" on only seeing the child and his or her behaviour in the room, then your ability to provide real, lasting help is critically endangered. In fact, I suggest that in most cases you are pouring water into a bucket with a hole in it and, in some cases, actually adding to the stress of a child's or family's life.

I believe that the systems approach is critical in working with children and adults. It is crucial to understand how systems work and how they react to stress and change. It is also important to consider not only the family system but other systems the child is encountering (i.e. the school system, boy scouts, siblings etc.). You and the child also form a system, and many of the processes described in systems theory will come into play between you and the child.

It is also true that the child himself can be seen as a system, searching for balance and belonging. For the child there are three major components in constant interaction with each other: feelings, behaviours and beliefs/attitudes.

In working with children the ideal situation is to work also with the family as a unit. This may require some individual work with some members, marital or couple therapy, sessions with the siblings, etc. However, you are always able to focus on the larger system and help it to absorb the individual changes and make the adaptation required.

In utilizing play therapy, there are several formats which I have followed in trying to incorporate the notion of systems. The particular approach I use will depend on my assessment of which may be most effective, coupled with which is most possible logistically, tempered by what is realistic. Certainly, one of the greatest barriers to working with a family as a whole is the lack of involvement from the parents. This may be due to a parent not being available or absolutely refusing to speak with you. In some situations you may find yourself working with a child who is in alternate care (i.e. foster care, group home, etc.). Working with the current family system is an option that for a variety of reasons may not be possible.

The models or approaches I have utilized include:

1. **Working exclusively with the whole family.**

   This constitutes a pure form of family therapy. However, even in this forum, I would make use of play techniques.

2. Working with the child individually as well as with the family.

When the family is open to involvement but their resources are limited for the moment, and the child's behaviour is providing more stress and drain than the system can manage, I will see the child individually in play therapy and meet with the family for family therapy.

Again, depending on the resources available within the family, the actual scheduling of the child versus family meetings will vary. Some children I will see in several sessions before having a family session, others I will conduct weekly play therapy sessions with weekly or bi-weekly family therapy sessions.

With these families, my initial focus is on helping the family system concentrate on re-energizing and feeling a sense of hope. Without energy, there is little chance for change.

3. Working with the child, subsets of the family and the family as a whole.

Where certain subsystems seem to be locked into a very rigid relationship or pattern of interacting, I will arrange to see that subsystem alone. For example, in a family with two children, a boy age eleven and a girl age thirteen, it appeared the alliances within the family had taken place along sex lines. The general pattern which followed was Mom and Sue against Ron and Dad. This alliance prevented issues belonging to the children and issues belonging to the parents from being addressed effectively.

My decision, in consultation with family, was to meet with mother and son, father and daughter, husband and wife, and family.

4. Working with the child and the part of the family which is available and open to involvement.

In many cases you will find that one parent, or only some of the siblings, will make themselves available to be part of the treatment. In this case the motto is, "something is better than nothing." The absent members will usually attempt to sabotage any changes, but by utilizing a systems concept you are able to consider this and try to work with the members who are not there through those who are present.

5. **Working with the child and his/her siblings.**

At times you will find it useful to see the child with his or her siblings. This allows you a very revealing glimpse of issues such as roles, rules and communication patterns within the family. It also allows for some strengthening of resources (alliances) for the "identified patient".

6. **Working with the child and peers (group work).**

Where family members are not accessible, one of the other powerful systems a child is involved with is the peer system. This can be engaged through group play sessions. Since self-esteem and peer relations are common themes you will work with, this becomes an interesting option to consider.

7. **Working with only the child.**

Where it is not possible to work with any other system, you may only be able to see the child. In this case you need to consider the systems the child is engaged in and conduct your therapy and set your therapeutic goals based on this.

Your understanding of systems theory and the larger picture of human development will allow you to have a greater and more lasting impact on the clients you serve. Through seeing the linkage, sequencing and patterning of behaviour you will be in a better position of aiding the system to change. You will also be in a better position to check your sense of anger and frustration when you meet resistance. Resistance, rather than being a conscious thwarting of therapeutic interventions, can be seen as a signal that you need to consider the ramifications of change for the system. "Because change must be coped with, a family system which does not have functional ways to assimilate it will have dysfunctional ways. Generally speaking, a system which has rules requiring that the present be seen in terms of the past will be dysfunctional. If the rules of the system can be changed to meet the present, it will become functional. The dysfunctional family, when confronted with change, produces symptoms." (Haley, 1971, p 2.)

The implication of this for those working with children is amplified by the finding that the symptom bearer in a family is frequently one of the children.

There has been some recent literature written on trying to blend the idea of individual psychology and systemic theory. I feel that to be the most effective you need to understand both and be able to blend them into your therapy. "The question is often raised as to whether a symptom always serves a function in the system or whether it may be a reaction to a situation outside the family, such as work, school, or social relationships. Although the origins of a symptom may be rooted in an outside event, its persistence would indicate it is being used by the family in some ongoing transaction." (Papp, 1983, p 10.)

For example, a child is killed in a car accident and the mother becomes extremely depressed. This reaction seems quite within what one would expect and it would be quite acceptable for her to consider individual counselling or therapy to help her through the grief. However, if the family system re-organizes itself around the depression, with the depression manifesting itself as a necessary family ingredient (the family becomes very close, father becomes more responsible and involved, etc.), then a systemic approach may become necessary. If not, the system will resist the loss of the depression which is now serving an important function.

In play therapy, specifically, I try to involve the parent(s) as much as possible. To accomplish this I have had several options:

1. **Parents as consultants.**

   I enlist the support of the parents as consultants and peri- odically meet with them and the child to review progress, or lack of progress. I tend to use this with cases where the child and parent(s) have a good relationship with a solid level of trust.

2. **Parent as observer.**

   I have some parents observe sessions from behind the mirror, (with the child's knowledge). I use this for parents who have a good connection with their child but little understanding of the needs of children. I have used this in a number of cases where the child has assumed a parental role and does not "know" how to play (often referred to as a "parent-child").

3. **Parent as trainee.**

I undertake to "train " the parent(s) to "play" with their child. This may begin with the parent observing a few sessions, then moving to being in the room observing, to being in the room participating, and finally I move out of the room and the parent remains with the child. I tend to use this with parents who have become very drained and obtain little enjoyment from their child(ren). In completing genograms, and looking at generational material, one will often find that these parents had little "childhood" themselves.

In each of these cases, the primary focus of therapy is on the relationship between parent and child, rather than on an issue within the child. This does not mean that I do not deal with those internal issues, but overall it really gives a different venue for the session and much of the play and activity will take a different course from what we may call "pure" play therapy.

In recognizing the importance of systems the therapist himself can utilize natural processes and powers, enhancing the intervention. Ignoring this can create a struggle for power and control, stimulate resistance and impede a child's development and growth.

Triangulation

Last summer, my younger sister, Marina, was married and my daughter, Natasha, who was almost three at the time, was asked to be a flower girl. Her four year old cousin, Zoe, was also asked, with five-year-old Geordan acting as ring bearer. Zoe and Natasha play extremely well together, Natasha and Geordan play extremely well together and Zoe and Geordan play extremely well together.

At the rehearsal, all went quite well; each of the children were led by an adult down the aisle and with several other children around they played without concern for each other. However, at the wedding, Zoe, who was close to Geordan, decided to hold his hand and walk down with him. Natasha rushed forward to try to take his other hand but he was carrying the small pillow with the rings on it. Natasha was visibly upset but did finish her walk then grabbed Geordan's hand when Zoe let go.

When the wedding party was to walk off, Natasha rushed forward to take Geordan's hand and Zoe was left out. Zoe cried out in despair. However, for Natasha the damage had been done, she saw me and ran into my arms crying out, "Daddy, Geordan didn't marry me!"

Several months later, she still remembers this experience and constantly asks me, "But, Daddy, who's going to marry me?"

This story illustrates a clear case of an interactive process called Triangulation. Understanding the concept and dynamics of triangulation is critical in working with human relationships, especially within the therapeutic relationship. It is one of the specific concepts related to the systemic approach and to emotional functioning which I have found critical to consider.

As the label suggests, triangulation deals with relationships involving three units. Of course this is not a new concept and the special features that triads contain have been referred to for centuries. The familiar adage, "three's a crowd", is derived from the common finding that when a third person is added there is either conflict arising (with two against one), or one person is left out.

"Diplomats know that the international power balance is based on threes and the absence of one of the three creates a dangerous vacuum. (In 1892, a book was written about triangles based on the issue of power.) Freud "created" the Oedipus complex, a rare form of sexual triangle. He also spoke of the ego, the id and the superego, a form of inner triangle." (Fogarty, 1975, p 11.)

Triangles exist in all families and in relationships outside of the family. The intensity of triangles, the function of the triangle and of the triangulated person and the role of the people within the triangle, vary dramatically. Often we are quite able to function within our various triangles and are unconscious of our influence in or by this system.

In general, a triangle is formed when a twosome undergoes stress which endangers their intimacy. In order to avoid further deterioration, a third person is added (or adds himself) to take stress off the original system. This is known as triangulation. One form of taking on or placing the burden on a third party is commonly known as scapegoating. We can find endless examples of scapegoating in our own lives and in our communities, whereby a twosome is able to maintain their relationship.

Scapegoating is not the only process which takes place in a triangle. Coalitions, alliances, punishment and creating intimacy are only some of the goals which a triangle is able to achieve. Consider Jenny, who is interested in Peter but he tends to take her for granted. She develops a relationship with Ted, making sure that Peter is aware, and just has a good time. Ted is probably not aware he has become triangulated in order to help Jenny preserve and, in fact, strengthen her relationship with Peter. Of course, Peter may decide to take no notice, but if he has some emotional connection with Jenny, her plot has a good chance of success.

Triangles are also intergenerational and, in fact, it is these triangles that usually carry the most impact. Unresolved issues, which require the formation of triangles, can be passed on for many generations, without the awareness of the recipients. This is known as the funnel effect. "The funnel effect states that the unresolved difficulties literally pass on to the next generation until they reach the apex of the funnel. At this point, symptoms develop. When one runs into a triangle that is so emotionally fixed that it seems beyond the possibility of change, one can be certain that this problem is the apex of an overloaded generational series of triangles." (Fogarty, 1975, p 15.)

The most important thing to remember is that in human relationships the relationship between three parties who have formed a triangle is an emotional one and revolves around an emotional process. As such, triangles are caught in a system which defies logic and cannot rationalize or be rationalized. "There is no victimizer or victim. The notion of causality or who started it is a chicken/egg question. It is irrelevant. Emotional systems deal with process and not cause." (Fogarty, 1975, p 13.)

In families, where members who are triangulated become exhausted or no longer provide the balance, the family may attempt to draw in people from the outside. A school principal, the doctor, a minister, a social worker or psychiatrist are all vulnerable to becoming a part of a triangle (we sometimes refer to this colloquially as being 'sucked in').

I recall in my first few years of practise, I wondered about every other professional's competency since almost everyone who came to see me, who had seen another counsellor or therapist, berated that person for being so terrible and ineffective. I was unable to see, at that time, how the professional had become triangulated, allowing the clients to maintain their relationship by dealing with a common enemy.

Minuchin (1974) identifies three generalized types of triangles which are in operation in many dysfunctional families. These are:

1. **Taking Sides.**

   One of the members of the triangle, usually the child, is used to deflect conflict between the other two, usually the parents. Once the child has taken sides, he finds himself merged in the conflict with the parent he has taken sides against. By taking the position of one parent, he is seen as attacking the other. If he refuses to take sides, the parent who was expecting the support will see this decision as an attack or rejection of his position or relationship. The child is caught in a powerful bind and usually will develop dysfunctional symptoms.

2. **Detouring.**

Two of the members in conflict focus their attention on the third party and become preoccupied with that person's behaviour. As the twosome unites against the third, the tension between them decreases. Often the third person will voluntarily seek this position in order to preserve the relationship of the other two. This is very common for the acting-out or acting-in child whose parents are in danger of breaking up.

3. **Stable Coalition.**

In this type, two members join in order to exclude the third person. This often involves cross-generational coalitions (grandmother — mother against father). This form usually is seen where one of the parents has an enmeshed involvement with a child or with one of their parents. The difference between this and Taking Sides is that the third member is not attacked but excluded.

Since patterns in triangles are easily identified and have predictable outcomes, knowledge of this concept allows the therapist an advantage in intervention. Intervention is aimed at the twosome resolving their conflict and no longer require the third (often the child). Where direct intervention is not possible with the two, their triangulated third can be helped to respond differently and thereby force the two to search for different solutions.

It is a common phenomenon for the therapist to become triangulated in therapy. This may occur in one of the three forms above and if it does, it makes you impotent. (Minuchin, 1974, p 101-103.)

Knowing a triangle exists

There are several clear clues which can tell you if a person or system is caught in a triangle. These are:

1. When there is conflict between two people and focus is placed on this, is a third party, object or issue introduced?

2. Do members define themselves or do they use a third party to define who they are or what they think?

3. Are patterns repetitive? The son always takes the side of the mother. The underachieving daughter is always the one who is causing problems.

4. Can all members have different views or thoughts without coalitions or arguments arising?

5. Is there a change in feelings, issues, roles, etc., when one of the members is present or absent?

Triangles in Play Therapy

In play therapy you will be placed in a paradoxical situation. On one hand you want to prevent or demolish triangulation; on the other hand, your ability to understand and help the child will depend on the existance of triangles.

The first part is a given and you will seek, through family intervention and/or individual intervention, to free the child from a dysfunctional triangle. However, in the process of play therapy you will actually utilize triangles. In the chapter on techniques there is an example of using puppets to take on an antagonist or protagonist role. Here you can create a triangle temporarily in order to place the child in a particular role and increase or decrease the emotional process of therapy.

You will find that knowledge of triangulation and the ways people use a third party can help you identify when this happens to you. You will also be able to comfortably predict when this may occur. Parents, the child, teachers, doctors, co-workers, supervisors and other professionals may try to triangulate you or you may try to triangulate them in order to deal with a salient issue.

The important feature is not to become paranoid, not to pull yourself so far away that you become a non-feeling object and thereby negate any possibility of being emotionally drawn in. Becoming a robot or computer, I believe, is a greater evil.

By drawing upon your knowledge and experience in the areas of Systems, Triangulation and Transference/Counter-transference, you will be well equipped to limit the blind spots in treatment and maximize your clinical resources.

Transference/
Counter-transference

We are social beings and, as such, seek relationships to sustain us. This goal is achieved through our ability to interact and relate to others. In turn, we are influenced by how others relate to us.

This interaction process begins at conception. Recent studies reveal more and more about how external stimuli, such as music, dancing, emotional experiences of the mother, influence the growth and development of the fetus.

As children, our involvement with relationships is usually quite limited, and dependent upon our families. Our parents, as the primary adults in our lives, carry the greatest influence on how we learn to relate to others and the world outside. Brothers, sisters, grandparents, foster families and "significant others" may also carry different degrees of influence depending on their role and extent of involvement.

In our relationships, there are two main dimensions at work. One is our behaviour and the other is our feelings. As we interact, these two are in continual play; our feelings often having an overriding influence on how we act.

Since our learning, especially in our formative years, is primarily based on experience, we are restricted in our range of response. We constantly record experiences and when faced with a new situation, search for a record or reference to provide a frame for our response. Those recordings or references are usually unconscious and serve to enable a person to adapt to new situations or environments. However, these same references also tend to lock us into responding to certain situations in a particular or predictable fashion (especially those which stimulate strong emotions). "Of the innumerable patterns of human interaction each person tends to select a few favourites. From earliest childhood, (primarily as a result of our interaction with our parents), we develop a constellation of patterns of relating to others that are unique. As we grow older these patterns become strengthened and we tend to utilize them in preference to others that may either be absent from our repertoire or have lower priority for utilization. Some of these patterns of interaction are healthy and enhance our effectiveness in life. Others are maladaptive . . . These patterns are strongly repetitive — almost reflexive in nature. Accordingly, in new situations we tend to use the old patterns even though we may suffer significantly because of our injudicious reaction." (Sarason, 1972, p 20.)

Each of us has both adaptive and maladaptive references which come into play from time to time. When we bring these patterns of response into a new relationship or situation we call this transference. Thus the person is "transferring" his experience from the past into one in the present.

"Transference involves the displacement of patterns of feelings and behaviour originally experienced with the significant figures of one's childhood to individuals in one's current relationships, often the therapist." (Sarason, 1972, p 62.)

The following are some examples to illustrate the principle.

The seven-year-old girl, who was sexually abused by her father, relates to the therapist in seductive ways (i.e. rubbing his leg, sitting on his knee).

The eight-year-old boy, who has been placed in foster care because of severe physical abuse. After three weeks, the child is removed as the foster parents, who have always been gentle and patient, fear abusing the boy.

The twenty-six-year-old woman, who becomes upset when praised by her employer. When she was a child, her mother rarely said anything positive and, if she did, it was followed by severe criticism or complaint.

In each of these examples, the person is responding to a new situation in an old way. Each has unknowingly become locked into dealing in a consistent and predictable way with a particular situation. When this "transference" is maladaptive, inappropriate or prevents a person from healthy growth and development, therapy needs to focus on the source "reference", which keeps the individual(s) from establishing new interactional patterns.

Each of us is a unique person, and we all have our own unique set of recordings and references. Each of us also places different weight or reliance on these references. Therefore, in some situations I may be able to shut off an old reference or create a new reference quite easily. In others, my reflex action predominates and controls reactions without my awareness.

A cornerstone of therapy is helping a person to do just this, create a new reference which is adaptive for that individual. "Through transference experience the analyst can help his patient to recognize defenses which made sense in the past, but do not belong realistically in the present. The analyst can also help the patient to become aware of his attempts to re-create old traumatic situations over and over again in each new relationship." (Haworth, 1964, p 18.)

I recall being told of an experiment when I was in university. Researchers were looking at how senses were adaptive to the environment and, in one test, had a special set of lenses attached to a person's eyes so that everything was reversed, like looking in a mirror.

Initially the person bumped into things, got out of the wrong side of the bed, was quite disoriented. Very quickly, though, the brain made necessary adjustments and the subject was able to function as well with the lenses as before.

Then the lenses were removed, and the subject again bumped into things and was quite disoriented. An adjustment period was needed before the person could function without the lenses.

In new situations, therefore, we are often unable to respond immediately in the most appropriate way. Most of us are able to adapt, but a great many will keep bumping into walls. Children, though young, have these references also and are easily locked into patterns of behaviour or interacting.

The therapist must also be aware of the process of counter-transference, which essentially is the same as transference, except the therapist has a recording or reference switched on by the client and the therapist acts in a pre-determined sequence with him. "The therapist must be careful about forming a counter-transference, which involves the unconscious motives which the therapist might have acted out in his relations with the client. If the therapist has not developed adequate insight into his own personality dynamics then very possibly he will act out an image of his own, using the patient as substitute figure." (Rychlak, 1975, p 72.)

I believe it is impossible to prevent this from occurring at some time or other in therapy. Certain people touch us in ways that are difficult to explain, raising feelings of anger, sadness, anxiety, etc. We cannot turn ourselves on and off in therapy. However, we can recognise the phenomenon of transference/counter-transference, be aware of it when it is occurring, and know how to move beyond it (or utilize it for therapeutic purposes). This phenomenon is relevant for those who are working with children, although there has been some debate as to its direct applicability. "In my work with children, I have been struck by the fact that the child's responses to me and my reactions to his/hers have many similarities to the equivalent phenomena with adults. Yet transference and counter-transference phenomena, which are regarded as characteristic in analytic work with adults, have never really been acceptable in work with children. Thinking over this in terms of the controversy between Anna Freud and Melanie Klein, I have felt that something important has been overlooked in the analysis of children . . . " (Haworth, 1964, p 243.)

I recall one eleven year old I was working with who was very resistant to therapy. I found in the sessions I was becoming frustrated and angry and usually ended with some form of conflict between us. The child was taking karate and often took threatening stances with me. Unlike other children I had worked with, I was unable to manoeuvre, or even to develop options around this. Shortly after starting with the child, I visited my brother and went home feeling frustrated and angry. I was able to associate with the same feelings in the session and realized that the boy I was seeing fit how I would have described my brother when he was thirteen and I was ten (my brother coincidentally had taken karate at that time). With this awareness of the counter-transference which had taken place, I was able to get myself "unstuck" and the therapy could proceed.

There are several indicators which can be used as signposts for your therapy. This does not necessarily mean that transference/counter-transference is taking place, or if it is taking place, that it is unhealthy, but it does enable you to make the process conscious and accountable.

These indicators are:

1. An arousal of intense feelings from the child, especially if related to certain interactions.
2. An arousal of intense feelings from you, especially if these feelings linger after sessions.
3. The child's response is incongruent with the situation (i.e. "Would you like to play with something else?" The child shouts, "Leave me alone, you are always picking on me.").
4. There is little or no progress in therapy.
5. You are unable to find anything positive or likeable about the child, or you are unable to find anything inappropriate about the child.
6. You feel yourself acting more like a parent than a therapist.
7. Your view of the child is exactly the same as the parents' view.
8. In discussing the child in consultation or supervision you find yourself becoming emotional (angry, sad, anxious, etc.).

Transference/counter-transference is not an issue itself in therapy. In fact, it is a natural process enabling us to survive in the world. What is at issue is how to help those who have become "imprisoned" by their references and thereby unable to respond to situations appropriately.

Developing new references and accessing old references will be a continuous process through our whole life. As we help individuals become less rigid, and have more options to move from one to another, the individual is better equipped to handle our very complex and stressful society.

One of the advantages and disadvantages of working with children is that they are still within direct parental influence. On the positive side, this means that the interactional base is still in process and that the system can be accessible to changes. You are usually able to meet with the parent(s) and obtain first-hand information. You are also able to work with the system as a whole to provide opportunity for growth for the family, not just for the child.

The disadvantage is that the child may have fewer options for change. Should you be working with a child whose family members are not making themselves accessible or are unwilling/unable to look at their own references, you must recognize the child is still living within that system and you must not set him up for further despair. "All patients, regardless of their age, have to be helped in treatment to gain a clearer view of their parents . . . The child has to be helped to see that his parents, like all other human beings (including the therapist) are not perfect . . . Helping the child become clear regarding which personality traits of his parents are assets and which are liabilities can be very useful." (Gardiner, 1975, p 31.)

For example, I was working with a ten-year-old whose mother, overwhelmed by day-to-day living, provided little nurturing. His mother, at the time, felt unable and was unwilling to participate in sessions. As we progressed in play therapy, Jon was able to ask for attention and affection. It was necessary, though, to help Jon distinguish between those who could and those who could not provide that for him. In this case, the teacher, an aunt and I were able to, his mother was not. Jon was able to develop an appreciation of this, including an appreciation of what his mother was able to provide him. This was done without setting up Jon or his mother with false expectations of each other.

Therapists need always to be aware of their tremendous influence in creating references that the child will carry with him. Many of the children you see will take on your behaviours in an effort to become closer to you. "Just as a child imitates his parents and acquires many of their traits (both adaptive and maladaptive), he will tend to identify with the therapist if the relationship is a good one." (Gardiner, 1975, p 32.)

Several years ago, I had an interesting experience which illustrates this point well. I was working with a ten-year-old boy who was constantly blinking, twitching his nose and scratching. His mother and teacher found these habits very disconcerting, although they were not the primary reason for referral. Although we did not focus on his tics directly, as the child progressed in treatment his nervous habits ceased.

When treatment ended the mother reported improvement in all areas of her son's life, except she found he was constantly "cricking" his neck. This was a new behaviour and seemed to appear in the last two weeks of treatment and had continued since then.

As I was speaking with the mother I became conscious that I was "cricking" my neck, and realized that for the last month I had a sore neck and so would shift it every now and then. The boy, had in fact, picked up his new "habit" from me and continued this after our relationship had come to an end.

Transference, and especially counter-transference, are often very difficult for the beginning therapist to catch quickly and counteract. The therapist may find it very useful to discuss with a supervisor, consultant or co-worker the various signs that the process is taking place. Often you will require a third party to provide input and feedback from an outside point of view, which may be provided by video tapes, audio tapes or live supervision. Discuss your feelings with colleagues/supervisors/teams, etc. Ask others about their experiences with this phenomenon. Finally, think about those people you are close to and enjoy, and those you find 'bothersome'. Reflect on why this is and see if there are any old recordings being switched on.

Hypothesis-Building

"A simple case, and yet in some ways an instructive one,"
Holmes remarked as we travelled back to town . . . "It was clear
to me from the strength of her glasses that the wearer must have
been very blind and helpless when deprived of them. When you
ask me to believe that she walked down a narrow strip of grass
without once making a false step I remarked, as you may
remember, that it was a noteworthy performance. In my mind,
I set it down as an impossible performance, save in the unlikely
case that she had a second pair of glasses. I was forced,
therefore, to seriously consider the hypothesis that she had
remained in the house. On perceiving the similarity of the two
corridors, it became clear that she might very easily have made
such a mistake, and in that it was evident she must have entered
the professor's room . . . "

(Conan Doyle, 1905)

There are three distinct but interwoven stages of therapy:

1. Assessment
2. Treatment
3. Termination

Although these may be difficult to distinguish from each other in the actual content or process of therapy, there are significant differences in the way you are looking at, packaging and utilizing the input and output of each.

For effective therapy, your assessment skills must be well tuned. However, assessing by itself is a relatively easy process and generally based on the gathering of information. Many therapists I have been in contact with see the goal of assessment as having as much data as possible and collecting enough to write a three-volume biography of the client. However, they still find they have little or no direction when it comes to intervention strategy and they are often led to gathering more data.

It is not the gathering of information which is the crucial goal in assessing, but rather the formation of a hypothesis which will then dictate what to do with a particular client. This in turn dictates the information you need to collect and the 'trails' you need to follow.

To put it simply, your task is to be a Sherlock Holmes: following clues, noting the necessary, eliminating the unnecessary and then developing a hypothesis to work from.

Children come to us with a variety of problems or symptoms, described by a parent or other adult. In order to help, in the systems approach, we need to make sense of what function this symptom or problem serves for the child and/or the system he is engaged in.

One key point to remember, though, is that hypotheses are not the be all and end all. They are your 'best guesses' at what may be happening and it is your responsibility to check and re-check them in order to validate or invalidate them. As treatment (or assessment) continues, hypotheses should be formed and reformed continuously. "The therapist may modify the formulation many times as new information is gathered from the family. It is not necessary to wait for a definitive hypothesis before intervening, as many times only the interventions themselves produce crucial information. Nor is it necessary for the hypothesis to be absolutely accurate; it must only be relevant to the family and to change." (Papp, 1983, p 17.)

The hypothesis is the connection you make between the information you gather and the problem you are addressing. In our daily lives we are constantly using this process. When you hear a loud noise in the house, you take this information and begin to develop a hypothesis as to the source. Your reaction(s) will depend on what you have formulated. Let us imagine you hear a loud bang. What are some of the hypotheses which are possible?

1. One of the children is up (if you have children).

2. Something fell down (picture, etc.).

3. There is an animal in the garbage.

4. Someone is in the house.

5. Someone slammed down the hood of a car.

There are many other possibilities, depending on your exact location, volume of the sound, etc. However, it is clear that each will move you towards a very different action.

It is important, though, that you do not close the doors after forming a hypothesis; rather, you must develop automatic and ongoing methods to check it out in order to confirm or invalidate it. By doing this, you avoid going on "wild goose chases" with the client. In the above example, then, you would start with your "best" hypothesis and then project conditions to check it out.

For Example:

1. One of the children is up. If this is true, several things may help you confirm this:

    a) Is the noise followed by crying?

    b) Where did the noise emanate from?

    c) Was the noise consistent with this source?

    d) Can you hear any accompanying sounds (voices, footsteps, fridge door closing, toilet flushing, etc.)?

2. Something fell down. You may consider the following checks:

    a) Is the noise consistent with something falling?

    b) Where did the noise come from? Is there something in that room or outside which could fall?

    c) Have you heard the sound before?

3. There is an animal in the garbage.

    a) Is there garbage out?

    b) Has there been a problem with animals in the past?

    c) If it is winter time, are there tracks in the snow, or is the garbage can turned over?

4. Someone is in the house.

    a) Did you leave any windows or doors unlocked?

b) Can you hear any other noises?

c) Have there been other break-ins in the neighbour-hood?

5. Someone slammed the hood of a car.

a) Can you hear outside noises from where you are?

b) Are there cars parked nearby?

c) Can you hear a car starting?

As you set a hypothesis and check it out with further information, you are led to a plan of action. In the above examples your action can range from ignoring to checking the kids to calling the police.

If you find your "best" hypothesis is invalid (you check on the children and find them all fast asleep), you move to your next best hypothesis. You continue to do this until you have some validation.

In therapy, you will find this process invaluable and, as you utilize it more, it will become more fluid. In play therapy, your development of hypothesis is occurring throughout your sessions. How you respond to the child, what themes you choose, even the particular techniques you select, are affected by the hypothesis.

When developing hypotheses I consider several factors:

1. Who is involved in the problem?

2. What is the child's role?

3. What function does the problem serve (what does it do to help the child or family)?

4. What would happen if the problem disappeared?

1. Who is involved in the problem?

It is important to identify all the players involved in the problem being presented by the child and/or family. It is very common for the therapist to miss individuals who are not part of the interview or are not living in the house. Grandparents, absent parents, older siblings who have moved out, a nanny, etc., may all be critical players in the system. Several questions which can help to elicit this are:

    a. Who else is concerned about this being a problem?

    b. Whom does this problem affect or bother the most?

    c. Who would notice a change in the problem first, next, last?

2. What is the child's role in the problem?

You should really look at everyone's role and how each one is connected/inter-connected with the problem and the function of the problem. Is the child a scapegoat, parent/child, the family feeler, the connecter, the quiet one, the troublemaker, etc.? Is mother the protector, the helpless one, the martyr, etc.? Is father the enforcer, the outsider, the referee, etc.?

How locked in are these roles? Do members have a hard time moving out of them? In which environments do they come into effect?

The more dysfunctional a system is, the more rigid and inflexible the role set. "Children whose family role is limited to the reciprocation of the projection and who, in order to maintain a shaky identity, become the role set for them, whole and undigested, are likely to have the family role as the foundation of their personality and consequently are high risks for psychosis." (Framo, 1982, p 32.)

3. What is the function of the problem?

Remembering that each system seeks balance and homeostasis in order to continue to exist, we need to understand how the problem serves this goal. How reliant is the system on this problem continuing? The answer to these will give you a hint as to the degree of resistance you will face. "Generally speaking, symptoms are maintained or reduced to the extent that they serve relationship-system functions and are an integral component of and bonding force in the relationships. Symptoms which sustain relationships and are embedded in stagnant contexts are likely to be the ones most intractable to change . . . " (Framo, 1982, p 45.)

There are two over-all functions of a symptom:

    1. To maintain the system as it is and prevent change.

    2. To incite change and challenge the status quo as no longer capable of sustaining the system.

While the first seems to be more common, you will be approached by a number of children and families who have developed symptoms in order to ask for help, or to force attention by the system on its need for change. This may be particularly true for adolescent clients.

Examples of some system functions are:

1. The child's behaviour diverts attention from marital conflict.
2. The child keeps mother involved through anger, not allowing her to become depressed and suicidal.
3. The child expresses loyalty to his birth father by not accepting his step-father.
4. The child's withdrawn behaviour prevents her from being more hurt by not forming relationships which could be withdrawn by others.
5. Aggression keeps other children and/or adults from getting too close.
6. The child's self-esteem stems from his ability to make others laugh and so he becomes stuck in the role of clown.
7. The child's behaviour is a way of punishing the parents for lack of attention.

Countless functions or themes can be developed and can become the centre of your hypothesis. Of course, it is important to remember that one must first rule out some of the more basic sources of problem formation. This would relate to physical causation, which is not controllable by the emotional or psychological system. For example, a child may be bedwetting due to a bladder infection. A child may be doing poorly in school due to poor eyesight or a learning disability. A child may be stealing lunches from other children because he is hungry and has no food.

The child may also be reacting to an unsafe situation, and this presents special consideration to the therapist. It is crucial that the safety of the child be paramount in your work and an intervention strategy must take this into consideration. Where the issue is related to the parental abuse or neglect, the appropriate authorities must be involved, even if it means "losing" the contact you have with the child.

When in jeopardy, a child tends to have one of two behavioral reactions. One is to attract attention as a "call for help" or to "blow the whistle" on what is happening, the other is to maintain the secret and protect the family system.

When you find yourself stuck in finding a working hypothesis and things just don't make sense, you should follow up on one of the following possibilities.

    a. There is a basic issue of survival in play (safety, shelter, food).

    b. There is a secret and the child is involved in maintaining the secret. (Secrets go beyond family abuse and/or violence, though this is very common. It may also involve drug or alcohol addiction, criminal behaviour or mental illness.)

    c. There is a physical or neurological base to the problem.

4. What would happen if the problem disappeared?

One way to get a clearer sense of the function of a problem and to develop your hypothesis is to focus discussion and play on what would happen if the problem magically disappeared. The response, or lack of response will usually be quite telling. The following is an example of this:

CASE X

The X family came to the centre because of the constant fighting between the children and between the parents and children. Dave, age 11, was the "worst of the lot" and was physically and verbally abusive of other children in school as well.

When asked what would be different and how he would feel if the fighting stopped from now on, the seven-year-old, after a few moments of silence, cried out, "It would be kind of lonely and scary." After some further discussion it became clear that the fighting was the only source of contact family members had with each other. The prospect of having no contact was worse than the fighting they currently suffered. This became the working hypothesis and from it developed the major focus in family therapy and in play therapy of finding new ways to contact each other, rather than just eliminating the aggression.

Hypothesis-building suffers from two major problems. From one side there is neglect and/or avoidance. Often this skill is seen as too complicated, overwhelming or unnecessary. On the other hand, many make the process too complicated, overwhelming or necessary. The practitioner needs to find a balance between the two. At times you will find that your instincts or 'gut' feelings are what you initially build some of your hypthotheses on. There is no problem in this, in trusting yourself, as long as you do not let this trap you into "proving" you are right.

Training for this area can be facilitated through several avenues, including:

1. Reading fiction and non-fiction books (especially mysteries). Create a hypothesis as you read and see how it works out.
2. Watch sessions of others or yourself on tape.
3. Read literature on hypothesis-building.
4. Connect yourself to a supervisor or colleague who is particularly strong in this area.
5. Stand near a street corner and try to predict which direction pedestrians will take. Review why you made that prediction and what subtle things give clues.

As you use this skill more, it will grow stronger and you will find that you will be able to set hypotheses faster and more accurately.

As your skill develops, you will be rewarded with a richer therapy, with increased efficiency and effectiveness.

Termination

Termination of a therapeutic relationship, especially one with a child, requires a thoughtful, deliberate process to ensure the therapeutic process is complete. "The manner in which the therapeutic relationship is brought to a close will heavily influence the degree to which gains are maintained: failure to work through the attitudes and feelings related to the ending of therapy will result in a weakening or undoing of the therapeutic work." (Fox, Nelson, Bolman, 1969, p 53.)

The ending of the therapeutic relationship is really a form of death for both the client and the helper. The reactions which one can expect and predict follow those related to death and loss. Unfortunately, appropriate attention to this phase of treatment is still often avoided or neglected.

With each person you work with, your level and their level of involvement will differ. Some of your clients will not have been very much effected by the loss, where others will find the ending very traumatic. Some therapists continue to hold on to cases in order to avoid saying goodbye, others may close cases quickly in order to avoid the pain and stress of the termination process. Still others react with surprise to regression, anger, or sudden rejection from the client, unable to recognise these responses as part of a grieving process.

With children, this is even more critical. As you become more involved in play therapy, you will find that for most, if not all, children you see, a strong relationship forms, at least in the eyes of the child. You will discover that your impact on the child is both powerful and intense and you will have become one of the primary figures in his life. Couple this with the fact that many of the children you see have gone through difficult relationships where they are unsure of their position; they have experienced abuse, rejection and dishonesty. Finally, they have a relationship with someone they can trust, who cares for them, who has provided them with a place to deal safely with their fears and issues, and who is now about to leave them.

Much of what follows parallels material you may be familiar with on death and dying. You should review this and use it in a planned way with the clients you see. The exact process will differ slightly from child to child, adult to adult, family to family, depending on the signs and responses you receive. However, I suggest in all cases you go through the steps of termination as some of your clients will surprise you. On several occasions, the person I felt was least attached actually had the most dramatic reactions to our sessions coming to an end. Conversely, some of those I would have labelled overly-dependent had very little difficulty separating and moving on to a new phase in their lives.

Signs of Reaction to Termination

There are a number of clues that clients give you which suggest they are having a reaction to saying goodbye to you. These are not totally exclusive and several may occur for the same client. These are:

1. Apparent loss of interest.
2. Decrease in activity.
3. A sense of emptiness.
4. Missed appointments.
5. Increase in problems/crisis.
6. Avoidance in talking about termination.
7. Regression.
8. Intense affectual expression, including:

anger	fear
blame	anxiety
sadness	rejection
hopelessness	emptiness
helplessness	loneliness
guilt	

Parallel with grief work, some typical behaviours you may experience are as follows:

1. Ambivalent feelings toward you (love/hate).
2. Inability to criticize.
3. Regression.
4. Overidealization of therapist.
5. Identification with therapist or characteristics of therapist.
6. Expression of hostile feelings toward self.

Grieving is an automatic response to loss and is meant to be reparative. It is also an opportunity for growth. Although we do not look forward to experiencing losses in our lives, we can grow stronger from them when they do occur.

Every loss we experience, major or minor, prepares us for ultimate losses later in life. The ending of a therapeutic relationship, therefore, has an even greater significance as it carries two major goals. One is to provide an appropriate and meaningful end to the existing relationship and to allow the person to carry on the changes they have undergone. The second is to provide a powerful model, often the first one, for the client to be able to relate to in dealing with ending relationships.

Many aspects of our lives determine the intensity and duration of the grief reaction:

1. The quality of the relationship that has been severed.
2. The strength of the attachment.
3. The security provided by the attachment.
4. The degree of reliance on the person.
5. The type of relationship.
6. The previous experiences.
7. The life crisis prior to the loss.
8. The ability of the person to express feelings.
9. The intensity of ambivalence.
10. The number of other supportive relationships available.

Components of a Good Termination Process

In training therapists, I have developed a series of steps which can be followed or adapted as required. This provides a framework to ensure the termination process has been completed and can be used for children or adults. The main difference with children is that I weave each of these into the play session and use the various play materials to facilitate the different steps.

1. *Preparing the way.*

   Discuss the ending of therapy well in advance, increasing the amount of time spent on the topic of termination in each ensuing session. In the last four sessions focus solely on termination and related issues.

2. *Clarifying the reason(s) for ending.*

   Each termination session, go over the reasons for termination and have the child give feedback to ensure his understanding is accurate.

   When you question child patients about the fact that you will not be seeing them any more, you will find that many say you don't like them any more, or something similar.

   Your reaction should be to state firmly the real reason. Most of the time it will be along the following vein.

Therapist:	"Do you know we have only a few sessions left, Tony?"
Tony:	"Yep. Three more after this one."
Therapist:	"Do you know why you won't be coming in to see me anymore?
Tony:	"Yeh. You're too busy and have to see other kids."
Therapist:	"No, that's not why. You came to see me because you were having trouble at school and at home. Now you are doing okay and know how to keep things that way. So now it's time for us to say goodbye
Tony:	"I don't want to say goodbye."
Therapist:	"I know that. I have a hard time saying goodbye too. But sometimes that is just what we have to do.

So, do you remember why you won't be seeing me anymore?"

Tony: "Yep, 'cause I don't need any more help."

Difficulty in this area can be dealt with by using puppets or stories relating to the same experience.

3. *Identifying Feelings.*

It is important to help the child identify and express any feelings they have. Knowing the common reactions to loss, you can comfortably predict that there will be denial, anger and sadness. Through discussion, stories and play you want to cover three areas:

a. normalizing feelings

b. labelling feelings

c. expressing feeling

4. *Reminiscing.*

Review your beginning relationship with the child with such questions as: How did he first perceive you? What did you think of him? How did these perceptions change? Why did they change? I always get some response from the child to each of these questions, especially in the area of how my feelings changed for the child over the course of the first few sessions and why.

5. *Reviewing.*

Go over your work with the child. Specifically look at:

achievements

failures

problems which arose

begin to identify how achievements were gained

6. *Predicting regression.*

Predict regression. Tell the child he will have a number of feelings and attach these to the termination process. Normalize these reactions.

7. *Responding to regression.*

When the child does experience regression, label it and again relate it to the termination process. Emphasize the achievements and the ability of the child to stabilize when they have expressed their feelings.

8. *Believing in the child.*

Ask yourself if you believe the child can do well without you. If yes, demonstrate this by making changes in your relationship— make more demands on the child.

If the answer is no, then raise the issue with the child if he is able to comprehend. If not, discuss with team or supervisor.

If you do not believe that the client can do well without you, then there is unfinished business which must be cleared up before termination.

One of the difficult situations which may arise from time to time is when termination occurs prematurely, perhaps because you are being transferred, or the child is moving, or the parents, for whatever reason, withdraw the child from therapy. I will deal with this more later.

9. *I never promised you a rose garden.*

Don't make promises which are unrealistic or put a lid on the grieving process (i.e. "You can come to see me whenever you want." "Sure I'll come to your birthday party next year."). Many children will seek ways, often very novel, in maintaining contact with you. Although at times this may occur, I treat every case as if the last session will be the last time I see the child.

10. *I am all alone again.*

Talk about the fears the child has around your leaving. What does he imagine will happen? What can be done about it? Who can he go to for help or support? How can he do this? Do not undervalue the anxiety that a child may have or the extremity of the fear of a life where he no longer has access to you and the play therapy room. Recognize and accept these, as well as any other feelings, then help the child to recognize his own internal resources and other supports readily available to him.

11. *You taught me a lot about . . .*

Share with the child what you learned or gained from him and vice versa. You want the termination process to be a two-way street, and to give the child a sense of contribution to the relationship as well.

12. *I am afraid of the dark again.*

Predict that the child may try to find ways to connect to you again in therapy. Especially by having the same, or new problems. Make a game out of trying to think of how this can happen and what the possible reactions could be. Have the child pretend to be the therapist, come up with some ideas of how you can connect to the child.

13. *You never really did like me.*

Anticipate and label "low blows." In the termination phase the child can say and do things which are very hurtful. Some of this is because of the feelings welling up in the child. Some will be due to transference, or referencing. For many of us, including children, the most convenient and fastest way to end a relationship is through anger and rejection. The anger will cover up the other feelings of loss and project all responsibility for the loss on the other person.

If you are able to respond to this appropriately, you can help the child develop a new referencing to deal with goodbyes and losses.

14. *Let's make a cake — the recipe.*

With all of the clients I work with, my ending phase centres around the development of their recipe. This recipe is based on the changes and achievements which have been identified and provides the child with a concrete list of "ingredients" which can be brought out whenever they need it. I usually use the analogy of baking a cake to explain recipes.

Therapist:	"Have you ever baked a cake before?"
Child:	"No."
Therapist:	"Have you ever seen one baked?"
Child:	"Yep, my mom does sometimes."
Therapist:	"Does it always turn out good?"
Child:	"Yep, it sure does. Especially on my birthday."
Therapist:	"How does she know what to put in the cake?"
Child:	"She uses a cook book."
Therapist:	"That's a great idea. I guess that's a good way to make sure you put all the right kind of things in. You know, you kind of baked a cake here in our sessions."
Child:	"No, I didn't."
Therapist:	"I don't mean a real cake. But you know those problems you were having before. Well, you did all kinds of things different and so those problems aren't there as much. I bet we can write a cook book of how you did that, a cook book you can take home and use whenever you want."
Child:	"Alright."
Therapist:	"Do you have any ideas of what we could make the cook book out of?

I have three distinct sections to the recipe which is developed.

1. Recipe for maintaining the change.

2. Strengths or resources of the child.

3. Recipe for going back to the old problems.

I try to use the child's language as much as possible so that he can relate to it later on. The recipe goes home with the child so he can refer to it later. This is also very helpful for the parents, teachers, etc., who can use the recipe to remind the child of what he can do differently.

I also like to identify the recipe for going back to old problems to make this process more conscious. It is generally a mirror image of the recipe for maintaining change.

15. Tears are okay.

I am going to miss you too. Do not be reluctant or afraid to express your feeling too. It is okay to be sad or angry. It is okay to cry. You are real too.

This is, in fact, the most powerful influence on the child, especially when he has no reference for a good termination process. Children learn much more through experience and through watching what others do.

16. Goodbye.

Say goodbye. Make sure you relate the goodbye to being a rewarding experience, a learning experience for both of you.

Usually, in my last session, prior to the child leaving, I will allow the child to pick one of a number of pre-selected toys in the play room to keep (pre-selected as you don't want the child to take the sand-box or the video camera). It is very typical for the child to take one of the toys which has some personal representation for him. Puppets are the most likely item. Which puppet is selected will depend on the significance the child places on it. Some children take a puppet which had taken a role parallel to the child's, others pick a puppet who has been their supporter, or even their antagonist during sessions.

Which toy they select or why is not really important. The selection allows the child to bring a piece of the play room, and his experiences in the play room, home with him.

A word of advice: always inform the parent or guardian of this to prevent a well-intentioned parent coming into conflict with a child, mistakenly thinking the child has taken a toy without permission.

You will need to adapt the above points in relation to the age of the child and the particular circumstances of the child. Younger children will be less able to verbalize their feelings or recipes, but they can work through them just as well through play materials.

As mentioned earlier, some terminations will be premature and will often leave the therapist with no opportunity to go through the process together with the child. There are several children to whom I have not had any chance to even say goodbye, as 1 was expecting them to return; something occurred which prevented it. In these cases, I would suggest sending a letter to the child which would contain all of the steps in the list above. If the parent of the child, or the child himself, is able to write back, you can go through the termination process by letter, or by phone. This is a process I did not use in the beginning of my work and it so happens the two cases which bother me the most are those two which were terminated prematurely due to parental circumstances and I was not able to reconnect. At that time, I also did not look for alternate mechanisms for saying goodbye.

Perhaps some day I will have an opportunity to meet these children again and express my feelings to them.

Techniques

There is an endless array of techniques available to be used or created by the therapist. This allows play therapy to be very adaptive to the child and to be culturally transferable.

In utilizing the various techniques one must first establish which of two main goals is being followed: assessment or treatment. Although the two need to co-exist, they do require a different approach to information being sought.

ASSESSMENT

In assessing, we need to be able to gather information and to make relationships between the child's view of his world and himself. This allows you to make a clinical decision about how to intervene (or not intervene). Even in non-directive therapy, the clinician must be analyzing the information and decide what response to make, whether it is verbal or physical.

To be most effective, assessing calls for observation skills which are multi-dimensional and relational. By this I mean you must look at the content, the process and the context in which behaviour takes place. To do this, we must ask ourselves a number of questions which lead us to setting a hypothesis, which in turn leads us to our intervention. The cycle then repeats itself.

Questions which I routinely ask myself are:

1. What is the behaviour which just occurred?
2. Does this relate to the behaviour which preceded? In what way?
3. What behaviour do I expect as a result?
4. What should I do next?
5. How does all this relate to the hypothesis currently in operation?

For example, Billy, age six, wets his pants in the room. There are a number of hypotheses I can establish, such as;

1. It was an "accident" and is not relevant.

2. It is an indication of a possible physical problem.

3. It is a reaction to something.

Depending on what I select, my reaction and interaction will vary from ignoring, to referring to a doctor, to making some intervention. If I do decide to make an intervention based on my sense that there is significance in the wetting I need to be more focused on what meaning it has.

If I look at the sequences of interaction in the session more closely, I can develop an assessment and a resulting hypotheses:

- Billy was playing with the Legos and asked if he could take home the house he had made.

- I asked him if he remembered any rule about that. He shrugged and replied, "Oh, yeah, I can't take toys home."

- Billy then went to draw some pictures. Suddenly he crumples up the drawing and shouts out, "I can't draw anything anyway." He then sits down and announces that he "peed his pants".

How do I react to this information? There are a tremendous number of possibilities, some of which are:

1. To ignore the incident.

2. To relate his wetting to being angry about the Legos.

3. To relate his wetting to his self-criticism.

4. To reframe his wetting by putting it into an affectual context.

5. To mirror his behaviour and throw out my drawing.

6. To retrieve his drawing and ask if I can keep it.

7. To redirect his attention.

8. To move into an open discussion about what he is feeling and/or thinking.

The key is that I need to base my reaction on how I assess the wetting and the child throwing his drawing out. How does this connect to the Legos and to previous sequences and sessions? Does this fit with the current hypothesis or call it into question?

Other questions which can help in your assessment are:

1. Is this behaviour common or is it something new?

2. Does the child have an expectation on me to react in a certain way (i.e. reject, nurture).

3. What might the child be getting from his behaviour (i.e. revenge, attention, isolation). How does this relate to previous information about the child and his/her family?

An important point is not to become overly anxious to be "right" and not make mistakes. The fact is that there is no fool-proof way to guarantee we assess and hypothesize correctly all the time. We can, however, make sure that we are always checking ourselves and, if unsure, gather additional information to aid in our intervention design. It is important to remember that you don't have to panic about having missed a "window". It is clear to me that the problems or issues displayed will present themselves again if they are meaningful, maybe in a different form, but they will undoubtedly arise.

There are numerous techniques which can be utilized to provide helpful assessments and direction for treatment. I would like to discuss two of these as examples.

CHECKERS

One of the most powerful techniques for therapists to master is the use of checkers for assessing and treating children and adolescents. I will focus on the area of assessment; however, it will be clear to the reader how this can be adapted for treatment as well.

There are a number of qualities which make checkers an excellent medium to use in play therapy. These are:

1. Most children can play checkers at least fairly well.

2. It is a very easy game to create if you are ever missing the pieces (i.e. bottle caps, pieces of paper).

3. Moves are fairly simple and happen in quick succession.

4. Several games can be played in a short period of time.

5. It is easy to detect whether the player is using planning and strategizing.

6. It can induce a number of common therapeutic themes, such as:
   - winning and losing
   - aggression and passivity
   - domination and being dominated
   - acceptance/non-acceptance of defeat/winning
   - honesty and cheating
   - trust and distrust,
   - ability to risk

7. It is within a child's abilities to "win."

8. There is room for dialogue.

In my use of this technique, I usually try to play at least three games with the child. One game I lose, one game I win, one game I draw. The order of these often depends on the age of the child and the clinical assumptions at the start. For younger children I tend to lose first. I also do this for children who have a strong need to win. For me to win first would probably mean not playing the second game.

There are a number of observations which I make of the content and process of play which then lead to an assessment and hypothesis. These are:

1. What colour does the child choose, how important is it for him to have that colour? Will he take the other colour? For example, one girl I was working with would only play with red since she associated the colour black with being bad. As she began to feel better about herself she was able to play with either colour. A young boy had the opposite preference and would only play with black. Black was seen as bad and powerful. The theme I worked on in his play therapy was his need to be in control and in power over others. He saw his "bad behaviour" as a way of accomplishing this.

2. Who goes first and how is this selected? Some children always want to go first, others never. Others seek some method of selection (i.e. coin, turns, pick a number). If there is a method does the child ensure she will win or you will win. Does the child trust you or ask you to trust her? (i.e. I'll think of a number between one and ten. If you get it you're first.)

3. Does the child purposely lose? Is she afraid to "take" one of your pieces? Does she sacrifice her pieces?

4. Is the child absorbed in winning? Can she accept losing one of her pieces? Does she give up, cheat or try to change the rules?

5. Is the child ritualistic, always making the same moves and the same mistakes?

6. Is the child open to learning something new?

7. Is the child strategizing and thinking ahead?

8. Is the child able to accept your win or your defeat?

9. Does the child play with energy and with interest? Is the child reserved and unenthusiastic?

10. Is the child reacting to your moves, considering them and making alterations in his? Or is the child only seeing his pieces and making moves independent of any changes around them?

There are many other permutations, but you should now be able to see how they can help you develop an accurate picture of the child. On top of the content and process you are also able to inject comments, questions, statements, etc., as you play (i.e. "Boy, you sure seem angry every time you lose a piece"). Personalities and relationships can also be given to the pieces to draw more from how the child develops this.

> Therapist: "My man here is afraid to move because you will probably end up taking him."
>
> Joan: "I don't think I will take him. Maybe if he moves over here I can move this guy and then he doesn't have to worry."

Contrast this with Frank who had a very similar scenario presented:

> Therapist: "My man here is a little afraid to move because you will probably take him on your next move."

Frank: "He better be scared, because I'm going to throw him in the dungeon and never let him out."

There is one pre-requisite to using checkers with children. You need to be a moderate player yourself. Even then, you may find some surprises as I once did with a very bright nine-year-old. The problem was I could not win. He was just too good at the game. Although this in itself told me some things and gave him a great deal of satisfaction, I simply moved on to another technique.

MUTUAL STORY-TELLING

A favourite technique I use resulted from a combination of enjoying metaphors and therapeutic stories and reading Richard Gardiner's work (1975) on the "Mutual Story Telling Technique." Although, at times, some children have been slow in engaging in this technique, everyone I have used it with has become wrapped up in the stories and has provided me with a powerful medium to assess and stimulate change.

In the version I use most often, I have a number of plastic animals, made up of farm, zoo and jungle animals. There are baby animals and adult animals, usually several of each to allow for family configurations.

To give a little more of the flavour of a game of chance, and to build in more creativity, the animals are mixed up in a bag or box and each of us takes a turn picking two, three or four animals to tell a story about. Each story must have a beginning, a middle and an end.

The child may set up a scenario for the animals, and have a few moments to do this and think of a story. Inevitably, the stories the children tell will carry all the themes that are issues for them and almost always will end in death and destruction. When it is the therapist's turn to tell a story, it is necessary to process the child's story and to inject the same theme in the new tale. The ending, though, provides a healthy resolution to the problem. In this method of assessment, it usually becomes quite clear what struggles the child is facing in his life and how he sees himself and the key persons in his life. One of the tasks for the therapist is to try to figure out who the animals/characters represent in real life. Invariably, one of the figures will be the child. The others are usually family members, but can also be the therapist, a teacher, siblings, grandparents, an abuser, etc. In general, there are several basic ingredients for therapeutic metaphors/stories as described by Mill and Crowley (1986):

1. Develop the main characters within an environment similar to the child's.
2. Establish the problem in relation to the main character.
3. Identify the child's fears and negative beliefs as villains and obstacles, strengths and resources (possibly identified by the child), heroes or helpers.
4. Provide learning experience where the character expands the skills necessary for overcoming the forthcoming crisis.
5. Present the crisis and describe how the character utilizes the helpers and/or newly evolved skills to overcome the crisis.
6. Define the new identification, or sense of empowerment that the character feels, as a result of successfully moving beyond the crisis.
7. Celebrate the character's new-found worth as a result of his/her successful journey.

If the therapist is unsure about the child's theme, it is possible for the therapist to just tell any tale in relation to the animals chosen which ends appropriately. However, in working with children, you will find that there is a set of themes which are very common and in most cases the child you see will fit into one or more of them. These common themes are as follows:

1. Power/Control
2. Anger
3. Belonging (family, friends)
4. Sadness
5. Self-esteem
6. Fear
7. Loyalty
8. Loss
9. Change
10. Safety.
11. Role/identity

12. Guilt/blame (over/under-responsibility)

CLINICAL SKILLS

How you approach treatment will depend very much on the model, the beliefs and the range of modalities you are familiar with.

Before looking at the specific play techniques that are available to you, it is necessary to point out that the strategies used in other forms of therapy are constantly integrated into play therapy. Some common clinical skills that I feel are core ingredients are:

- Labelling
- Joining
- Reframing
- Mirroring
- Intensifying
- Defusing

Two valuable techniques have already been described in the Assessment section: checkers and mutual story telling. There are, again, so many different tools to be used I am unable to address them all. I would like to describe some of those I use frequently and feel should be in the repertoire of play therapists.

PUPPETS

Puppets have been a source of enjoyment for children (and adults) for centuries. In play therapy, puppets allow problems to be discussed, examined or acted out. Because of the removal of the issue from the child herself, the child is able to look more objectively, or to look without the same level of defense in play.

Puppets come in a variety of forms and sizes. From people to animals to strange aliens, with mouths that move, or hands that can clap or eyebrows that move up and down.

I find it is useful to have several people puppets and several animal puppets. The more sensitive the child is to dealing with issues, the more you want to remove the play from the real world; hence I would tend to use animal puppets.

There are so many different ways to utilize puppets. Some of the ways I have used them in play therapy include:

1. As a third person in the room to take on a triangulated role.

   This may be to make comments I could not make, to induce the child to challenge more or to challenge the child, to be the devil's advocate or to be a wise soothsayer. The puppet, therefore, can allow you to say things which could ordinarily place your relationship with the child in jeopardy.

As an example, the following is an excerpt from a session with a ten-year-old girl:

Therapist:	"Well, I guess it is really okay for you to be angry with me."
Puppet:	"I'm pretty angry with you, too. I thought you were Mary's friend. Why do you say things to her that upset her?"
Therapist:	"I think she knows that I care about her and I just want her to talk about her feelings with me."
Puppet:	"But, she doesn't trust you yet. How do you expect her to tell about that sort of stuff?"
Therapist:	"You don't think she can talk to me about her sad and mad feelings yet?"
Puppet:	"No way. I bet she feels just like me when I had trouble talking about my feelings."
Therapist:	"Why don't you tell Jane about what happened to you."
Puppet:	"Oh, I don't know. Maybe Jane doesn't want to hear about my feelings (turns to Jane) Do you, Jane?"
Jane:	(Looks at puppet) "Yes."
Puppet:	"But you might laugh at me, or you might not like me after I tell you."
Jane:	"No, I won't, Simon."
Therapist:	"I think that Jane is your friend. I think she would really like to hear about your feelings and that she would even help you with them."

Puppet:	(gives Jane a hug) "Thanks Jane, sometimes I need someone to talk with." (Simon then talks about holding his feelings and how he learned to talk about them and feel better).

After this interaction, Jane begins to share her feelings with Simon, starting with her being angry with me for making her feel sad.

2. Another version of the puppet talking with a child entails the puppet taking on the role of challenger.

   This is to intensify a child's feelings, or behaviour so that the therapist can become an ally and move towards a therapeutic goal. As an example, a segment of a session with Phil, age eleven:

Phil:	"I really don't care if anyone likes me or not."
Puppet:	(to therapist) "Hey, he's telling a fib."
Phil:	"I am not."
Puppet:	(to child) "Yes you are, yes you are." (to therapist) "He's trying to fool you. He does care. Sometimes he feels terrible inside because no one loves him."
Phil:	"I do not, shut up or I'll punch you."
Therapist:	"I think you've said enough, Ali."
Puppet:	"No, I haven't . Why won't he tell you about how he really feels? Why doesn't he tell you he wonders if his mom cares about him?"
Phil:	(Grabs the puppet from me and throws it in the corner) "You shut up, you stupid alligator."
Therapist:	(Goes to get the puppet and talks to him in the corner) "Why are you saying all those things to Phil? You are really getting him mad."
Puppet:	"He's not as mad as he is sad because it's true. He really does care, but he's so afraid no one really loves him he does things to hurt them." (Phil is covering his ears).
Phil:	"I can't hear you. I can't hear you."

Therapist:	"I am going to have to put you away, Ali. I am really mad at you that you would say such things to him."
Puppet:	"But I only say it because I care. I don't want him to feel bad about himself, and I want to be his friend."
Therapist:	"Maybe Phil doesn't want to change. Maybe he's tired of being hurt and just needs to be left alone.
Phil:	"Yes. Just leave me alone. Nobody likes me so I don't like nobody."
Puppet:	"I like you . And Greg likes you. Don't you care about us?"
Phil:	"Not about you."
Therapist:	"Phil, are you more angry or more sad about thinking no one cares about you?"
Phil:	"Both I guess. It's about the same."
Therapist:	"Who is it that makes you feel the most angry and the most sad?"
Phil:	"Mom."
Therapist:	"You know, I guess Ali was right, but you didn't like hearing what he had to say."
Phil:	"Yeah."
Puppet:	"I didn't mean to hurt your feelings, Phil. I really want to be your friend. Will you be my friend? Please?"
Phil:	"Okay." (We then proceed to a game of catch between Phil and Ali. The issue about caring, mother and feelings will be dealt with later through other play activities.)

3. Another method is to have the child speak to you through a puppet, or for each of you to speak through puppets.

The child's expression of thought and feelings will be based on his own experience and knowledge. This will provide you with tremendous insight and opportunities for the child to explore the issues and the possible resolutions safely. The puppets allow the child to move one step away from himself, and provide an environment of both safety and control.

Puppets can also be used in conjunction with storytelling, where the puppets become the narrator and characters. An extension of mutual storytelling has the child and therapist taking turns telling stories, or doing "puppet shows", for each other. After each story, questions may be asked of the puppets who were in the story, or the puppet may ask the child questions (i.e. "Why do you think Frank was so mad at me? Do you think I could have done something else?").

To become more effective in the use of puppet and storytelling, one should practice talking in different voices. I suggest to beginning therapists that they use a set of consistent voices, and a common set of puppets with consistent personalities. Find four voices that you can easily duplicate.

Changing your tone or using an accent are the easiest methods. The following are some voices and characters which may be utilized to simplify the task.

Voices:
   1. Talk through your nose (nasal).
   2. Accents
        a) Scottish
        b) French
        c) Southern (Drawl)
        d) Texan or cowboy
        e) Russian
   3. Talk in high pitch.
   4. Talk in low pitch.
   5. Whisper loudly (Godfather).
   6. Speak quickly.
   7. Speak slowly.
Characters:
   1. Bully
   2. Shy
   3. Clown
   4. Cheerleader

5. Questioner

6. Rationalizer

7. Peacemaker

Sometimes it will help to identify a puppet with a well known figure. This can make it easier to remember the voice and the character being used. A few suggestions:

1. Yogi Bear

2. Mickey Mouse, Minnie Mouse

3. John Wayne

4. James Cagney

5. Alf

6. Clint Eastwood

7. Goofy

To make the puppet (or animal) become a real personality in the play, *you* must treat the puppet as real. You need to amplify or exaggerate movement and speech in order to draw and keep the attention of the child. You know you are being effective when the child's eyes are focused on the puppet and when the child begins to treat the puppet as separate from yourself.

With older children, including adolescents, I have used puppets and stories in conjunction with the use of a video camera and frame the play as making a movie or television program. Children and youths become tremendously involved in the process and are especially thrilled at being able to watch their production later. This, in itself, adds to the impact of some of the stories and metaphors since you build in "instant replays" and "re-runs", leaving you a wide open field for questions, remarks, thoughts and 'what-ifs'.

There are three other tasks for you to improve your use of puppets. Practice, practice, practice. Use opportunities with children generally to talk through a puppet. Do impersonations, try talking without moving your lips (although this is not necessary it does add to the play). Check out the different puppets in various toy stores and select those which seem to have "character" or "life".

Please note, that though the examples outline a conscious process of dealing with problems and issues, play therapy is not dependant on whether or not the themes become conscious and verbally expressed. The power of play will have its effect on the child since the child is constantly interacting with, responding to and adapting to the world outside.

SAND PLAY

If you have ever sat on a beach you will have noticed that most of the children (and many adults) at one time or another will make sand castles. Or they might run their fingers through the sand, or dig little trenches. You might find yourself doing this as well, as I often do.

Children love to create with their hands, and sand, like clay, offers a perfect medium to allow for three dimensional self-expression. At the same time the kinaesthetic senses are stimulated through sand coming into contact with the hands and fingers.

For sand play, all you require is a box, with or without legs, filled with sand. You can have a small area which holds water, if you wish, or paint the bottom of the box blue to simulate water. A variety of play objects can be introduced for use by the child. A few suggested items are:

1. People figures, providing a wide range of choices (sex, age, culture, profession, etc.).
2. Vegetation such as trees and shrubs.
3. Animals, including domestic, farm, zoo and prehistoric.
4. Marbles.
5. Stones and small pieces of wood.
6. Vehicles, including trucks, cars, ambulance, fire truck, police cars, etc.
7. Buildings (or material to make buildings).

The role of the therapist in sand play varies, though there are three common stances:

1. Therapist as observer.

   The child is active in the sand play with the therapist close by in an observer role.

2. Therapist as narrator or commentator.

The therapist is still an observer in the process but is asking questions, stimulating thought, making comments or narrating, etc.

3. Therapist as partner.

The therapist and child are both active with the child providing the lead and directions. The therapist is interacting and expressing interventions through the sand play.

Instead of sand, you can use dried peas, rice or some other similar substance. However, I have found that sand provides children with the most diversity for creating their unique worlds.

The child is invited (or invites himself) to play with the sand box. He may introduce any of the miniature figures and is free to place them anywhere they wish. The resulting landscape or "sandscape" is a symbolic expression of the child's self and how he perceives the world.

One girl, age 6, produced a scene which had all the figures squeezed into a fenced area. The impression given was one of chaos, conflict and suffocation. In the very centre of the picture was a small horse. The child related that the horse was scared to move and all the other animals were thinking of eating it.

Melanie's parents, I was aware, were in the process of a divorce. I surmised from the sandscape that the parents were in tremendous conflict and Melanie was feeling anxious and unsafe. Family sessions were recommended in conjunction with the play therapy. The focus was to separate the parents' battle and some of the other family issues from Melanie. In subsequent sessions, the focus with the sand play was to create boundaries between different animals and people; to have fences with gates and space between various animals; to separate the zoo animals from the farm animals and from the pets. Within two sessions, Melanie produced a new sandscape which displayed her new perspective on life. She had various areas for different animals and the little horse was able to visit each area safely and without feeling anxious.

INTERACTIVE STANCES

One model which I recently developed, and am still developing, is based on my observations of the various interaction patterns which occur during the course of play therapy. I noticed that in the initial stages of therapy

Interactional Stance		Interactional Symbol	
ADAPTIVE	MALADAPTIVE	CHILD	THERAPIST
Following	Chasing	Child ➡	Therapist
Leading	Dragging	Child ⬅	Therapist
Independence	Isolation	Child ⬅ ➡	Therapist
Challenging	Hostility	Child ➡ ⬅	Therapist
Mutuality	Enmeshment	Child ⇄	Therapist

various children reacted differently to me, but at the end of therapy there were some common elements, in all their reactions. In reviewing these common elements and then assessing for these at the beginning of the treatment, I found that it was possible to distinguish which stances were in place for the child and which were not. The goal of therapy was then to concentrate on those stances which were not evident, or were being used to extremes, and utilizing methods and techniques which directed themselves well to strengthen the weak areas.

Although there are many interactional patterns which can occur, I have limited the model to five core categories. These are:

- Following/Chasing
- Leading/Dragging
- Independence/Isolation
- Challenging/Hostility
- Mutuality/Enmeshment

In the course of a session, the therapist is able to assess each of these stances through a variety of play mediums. In each of the stances you are looking to see how the child is able to relate to you.

Following/Chasing

For this stance, you are assessing whether the child is able to follow your lead when you play a game or move to a new activity. Deficits include being unable to follow or being very anxious and overly ready to do whatever you want. The following are examples that demonstrate the different interactions which can occur within the one stance. The examples involve playing checkers with three different children, all about age 8.

CASE 1

Therapist:	"Well, that was a good game, Joe. How about we play something different now?"
Joe:	"Okay, what do you want to play?"
Therapist:	"Either the sand box or the animals."
Joe:	"I think the animals."
Therapist:	"Okay."

CASE 2

Therapist:	"Sarah, I'm a little tired of playing checkers. How about we play something else?"
Sarah:	"I don't want to play anything else."
Therapist:	"Well, how about we play with the puppet or sand box, then we can play checkers again if you want."
Sarah:	(throws the checkers on the floor). "I don't want to play anything then."

CASE 3

Therapist:	"Well, Mike, how about we do something else?"
Mike:	"Great."
Therapist:	"How about puppets or the sand box?"
Mike:	"Whatever you want to do."
Therapist:	"Which do you prefer?"
Mike:	"It doesn't matter. Whatever you want."

There is a difference being displayed by each of the three. I would consider Joe to be showing appropriate "Following". Mike, on the other hand, is "Chasing" while Sarah is "Absent" as she is not showing herself utilizing the stance at all.

It is important that one sequence is not used to make a final assessment. You need to observe several sequences and look for a pattern, and for consistency of patterns. Mike, for example, should be consistently showing a pattern of chasing. I will check this out by seeing if he is able to make choices independently. If he is stuck in this stance I can make some further assumptions that he is probably unable to lead and unable to challenge.

Likewise, with Joe, I will want to see if he is able to show the following stance in other scenarios, including his own play. I will also see if he is able to move through the other stances when the situation presents itself.

Leading/Dragging

As the label suggests, this is the reverse of the Following/Chasing Stance. What you are looking for is the child's ability to make decisions, to give directions and to provide some leadership. Some of your clients will act very appropriately, while others will move into becoming very dictatorial or even abusive of you. Still others will show an absence of either end of the spectrum.

Independence/Isolation

Each child should be able to move between relating to others and being able to play independently. This stance would measure the child's ability or inability to do so. You will find a number of your clients unable to play at all, always trying to engage you or others. Some of your clients will move to the extreme of isolating themselves in their play. Sometimes there is a fine line between independence and isolation; however, the nuance is quite specific. For a child who is isolating herself, you will find very strong barriers to intrusion and an almost complete lack of awareness or tuning in to you or to stimuli outside of the world she is in at the time.

Challenging/Hostility

Each child needs to be able to challenge in appropriate ways. This includes questioning things he is not sure about, standing up for what he believes in, not accepting certain behaviours in others, etc. etc. Many children we work with are unable to challenge anyone, while others do so constantly with aggression, hostility and anger. This particular stance is one of the easier ones to identify, and often one of the more difficult ones to remedy.

Mutuality/Enmeshment

Each child needs to be able to relate to others, whether peers or adults, as equals in an exchange of conversation or information where there is a sense of just "rapping". There is a sense of self, a sense of "I am me, you are you and both of us are okay". Often, however, we will work with a child who feels unable to communicate with peers and/or adults in any balanced way. He may feel intimidated or shy, and say very little or nothing: there is an absence of mutuality. Other children we meet will be able to communicate, but there is no sense of individuation. They are overly concerned with what you think, what you are saying, what you want them to say or think, etc. I call this enmeshment.

In order to give some more specific guidelines and related activities to test out the various stances, the following schema may be helpful.

Following Stance	Identifying Behaviours	Common Themes	Activities to Use
Following	The child allows you to make choices and decisions but is able to make them as well. The child may ask for clarification or appropriately question a decision you make.	N/A	N/A
Chasing	The child places you in a position to make all decisions. The child is overly concerned about how you may react or feel. The child demonstrates little power or control over his life.	Safety/Trust Identity Belonging	Activities which call for the child to make decisions. (i.e. choose which colour you want, you pick a name, what do you want to do next?) Activities that make the child feel safe.
Absent	The child does not allow you to make any choices. The child does the opposite of what you say. The child gives no response	Power/Control Safety/Trust Belonging	Co-operative activities Following activities (ie. follow the leader, Simon says) Independent activites

Leading Stance	Identifying Behaviours	Common Themes	Activities to Use
Leading	The child can make choices independently. The child can consider your wishes but makes their own interest as important. The child can move from leadership to another stance easily.	N/A	N/A
Dragging	The child "forces" you to do what he wants. Rules are created by the child. The child does not consider or tolerate your needs.	Power/Control Anger Self-Esteem	Activities which help to build recognition of need of others. Activities to help build tolerance/patience. Activities which call on the child to follow.
Absent	The child is unable to demonstrate any sense of choice or power. The child remains stuck in another stance. (i.e. Following).	Power/Control Safety Fear Self-Esteem	Activities which try to foster the ability to make choices and lead.

Independent Stance	Identifying Behaviours	Common Themes	Activities to Use
Independent	The child is able to play without the therapist. The child is able to acknowledge the separations. The child is able to re-engage easily.	N/A	N/A
Isolation	The child is unable to play with another person and seeks to constantly exclude the therapist. The child ignores the presence of the therapist. The child avoids interaction with the therapist.	Safety/Trust Fear Relationships	Draw attention to the separation by creating "bridges" between the child and therapist (i.e. we are both playing with Lego). Eventually move towards interactive play.
Absent	The child is unable to play alone.	Belonging Enmeshment Fear	Create situations for very short periods of independent play—gradually increasing the time.

Challenging Stance	Identifying Behaviours	Common Themes	Activities to Use
Challenging	The child is able to compete appropriately. The child is able to disagree appropriately. The child is able to express anger or disappointment.		
Hostility	The child is in frequent conflict. The child sets up conflicts. The child has to "win". When in conflict, the child expresses an inappropriate amount of affect—usually anger. The child may try to break toys or hurt the therapist.	Anger Hurt Power/Control Belonging Trust	Modelling and labelling. Following activities. Activities that identify and express feelings appropriately. Activities that raise self-esteem.
Absent	The child has difficulty winning. The child tries to please and/or nurture the therapist. The child refuses to challenge and becomes anxious if a situation arises.	Safety Fear Self-Esteem Belonging Role Issue	Modelling Leading activities Activities that provide safe situations for child to disagree.

Mutuality Stance	Identifying Behaviours	Common Themes	Activities to Use
Mutuality	The child is able to play or interact with you as an equal. The child is able to initiate conversation. The child is able to identify and accept differences.		
Enmeshment	The child sees himself as an extension of the therapist. The child takes on characteristic traits of the therapist. The child has a hard time separating from the therapist or a favorite activity.	Identity Self-Esteem Power/Control	Modelling. Independence activities. Activities that build communication skills and life skills. Activities that work on strengths and resources of the child.
Absent	The child is unable to interact with you or a "friend". The child sees you as a threat or as a "puppet" to be used for his purposes.	Power/Control Safety	Modelling. Activities that build communication skills. Those that ensure child feels safe. Mutuality activities.

You will have noted that there are a number of overlapping areas which will probably be common to many of the children you see. As well, many of the areas suggest the probability of a stance for another area. For example, if a child is enmeshed, it is unlikely he will be able to challenge or lead. The goal in therapy opens up several options then. You can work on helping the child reach mutuality either by trying to diminish the enmeshment or by working on leading and/or challenging.

The more "appropriate" stances a child is able to exhibit the more "healthy" she is, and probably the less extensive therapy will be.

The ultimate goal is to give each child the ability to move between all the "normal" or adaptive stances. The play activities and the therapist's interactions and interventions will attempt to focus on those areas which are maladaptive or absent/deficit, giving clear direction to the therapy.

Modelling becomes extremely valuable as a technique, since many children have not had an opportunity to observe appropriate interactions in a safe, caring environment. Also, one should note that many of the interventions are not through direct conversation, but rather through metaphors, stories and play activities.

OTHER TECHNIQUES

As previously mentioned, there is an endless array of techniques and materials which can be used. Art therapy, music, dance, clay, dolls, blocks, lego, games, etc. can all be used effectively in the play forum.

What the therapist uses as his/her tool is less important than how it is used. The how must capture the playfulness of the child and be brought to life within her world. Many non-play objects can be made into play therapy materials in the right situation and with the right projection. The following are some examples.

Afraid of the Dark

Chastity, age 6, was afraid of the dark and wanted to stop being afraid. I noticed she liked to draw and introduced the Lite-Brite into the room. Lite-Brite is a toy with an illuminated pegboard; the child can insert translucent coloured pegs in the pegboard to make an illuminated picture or pattern. She played with it but I noted the lights should be out to really see her pictures properly. She turned out the light when the Lite-Brite was on. I then suggested she could turn off the Lite-Brite and then turn it on to see what it looked like. She did this and proceeded to leave it off for longer periods of time. We then played several hiding games in the dark and then, through a puppet, discussed fears.

Paper Chase

Martin, age 11, was not too interested in playing and spent most of the first session crumpling up paper and shooting it into the waste basket. I then improvised a basket ball game where we would see who could sink the most. I then proclaimed the game much too easy and began to fold the paper into a plane. I threw the plane into the basket and missed. Martin laughed and tried to make a plane but was unable. I asked him if he wanted to learn how. He said yes and I showed him several ways to make paper airplanes.

After a few minutes, I made a paper hat and then a little paper construction game which you open and close to reveal a message. Martin became very interested and asked how I learned about making things out of paper. I told him about origami and said that I wanted to learn more but was not really very good.

Next session, Martin, a poor achiever at school, a withdrawn and non-communicative boy, brought in a book on origami he had found in the school library. He delighted in being able to teach me how to make different shapes.

Noisy Time

Matt was a 7-year-old boy who was aggressive and loud. He constantly yelled and was very rough with the toys. I invented a new game for us to play each session. We called it quiet time and noise time. Every ten minutes we had to change to the other time. Matt would decide which he was to start with. When it was noisy time, both of us were as noisy as we could be. We had to remind each other to be noisy and to bang things around. Then, with quiet time, we did the opposite. But, I tried to ensure we played something interesting. When Matt asked to shorten the noisy time I resisted, saying we had to follow the rule at least until next session. At the next session we re-negotiated and made the first 5 minutes of each session the noisy time. Soon this disappeared and we negotiated that noisy time was not a good game anymore.

Limited Choices

One of the greatest parental and therapeutic techniques is called limited choices. Power and control are important for each of us and no less so for children. Often in giving direction, we polarize a person's reaction and are left in a power struggle with no real winner in the end. However, if you are able to place that struggle within the person, or to focus the person's attention on a limited number of options, each one being acceptable to you, then you have a valuable therapeutic intervention.

For example, some children you meet will refuse to come into the play room with you. Depending on the case, your style and the age of the child, you may choose a number of responses. One which I have used successfully is to give the child a choice (usually in front of the parent). "John, you have two choices, either you can walk yourself to the room or I can carry you." I have eliminated not going to the room as a choice and, whichever option he takes, he has made the choice. If I end up carrying him to the room, he chooses for me to carry him.

Another example is Corina; I want her to become involved in story-telling but she is quite resistant. In order to give her some "power", I intervene. "Corina, would you like to play with the puppets or with the sand box next?"

This particular method is not conducive to non-directive therapy, but if you are using an approach in which the therapist is active then it is a good one to remember.

As a play therapist, you must learn to make use of any material around you and make it into a game. You must also be able to inject any of your other therapeutic skills (labelling, reframing, paradoxical intervention, etc.).

Above all you must be playful and inventive.

Setting up a Play Room

There is no such thing as a standard, or even ideal play therapy room. Each therapist or program will develop their play room in relation to their biases tempered by the resources available. The following, however, are some suggestions to consider.

1. **The Physical Space.**

   It certainly is helpful to have adequate space, without being too small, too large or too closed in. I would suggest for individual work, a minimum of 140 square feet and a maximum of 400 square feet can be considered. If you are able to, it is helpful to have a one-way mirror to allow for observation by parents, consultants, supervisors, etc. A good sound system should be installed as well. It is not necessary to have the micro-phone hidden. I always introduce the child to the observation room, the mirror, microphone and any other equipment which may be utilized. I also explain who may be observing and why. This is done in a matter-of-fact way and, after a few minutes, is out of the child's awareness.

   The room should be light and brightly decorated. Child oriented posters, drawings made by children and colourful paintings, all enhance a room. The goal is to make the room look "happy" and "fun". If possible, have lots of shelving and drawers with a combination of open and closed areas. Toys should have some organization based on the storage area and be kept neat and tidy.

2. **Furniture.**

   It is best to have as much child-oriented furniture as possible— a small desk, child-size chairs, etc. Make sure the furniture is solid and can hold an adult. I will sit on this furniture as well. Often, the child is very amused by the fact that an adult will sit in a tiny chair. Usually, I will sit on the floor so that the child is either the same height or slightly higher than me.

A large blackboard or drawing board, either attached to the wall or on a portable stand, will be found to be quite useful and a common play format for children.

You do not need a lot of furniture in the room. In fact, only having what is necessary is better so that you leave space for the child's imagination.

3. **Toys.**

The list is really endless, depending on the preferences of the therapist. However, do not have an exhaustive number of toys in the room. Choose those which you find fit into the type of play you do and which will foster the entry of the child into his or her world.

The following are two lists. One is for toys which I consider more essential for my therapy and the second is for those which are more optional. Only feel guided, not limited by this, though.

Essential Play Items	*Optional Play Items*
Plastic Animals (Zoo, Farm, Prehistoric, Domestic)	Trucks, Cars
	Wooden Blocks
Baby Bottle	Clay
Nerf Ball	Costumes
Sand Box	Dishes and Utensils
Doctor's Kit	Finger Paints
Doll House and Figures	Games (Snakes and Ladders, feel wheel, etc.)
Legos (or other building systems)	
Checkers	Flashlight
Puppets (people and animals)	Keys
Drawing Materials (crayons, paints, felt markers)	Musical Instruments
	Guns, Weapons
Physically Correct Dolls	Mirror
Dolls	Pillow, Blanket
Telephones (at least two)	Baby Carriage
	Play Money

Watch out for having games or toys which allow the child to isolate themselves or prevent themselves from playing. A deck of cards, story books, and puzzles can sometimes be converted into something therapeutic, but they also can be used to keep the child locked up. If I find this happens, I will remove that particular toy so that it is not available the next session. This leaves the child with having to make another choice, hopefully one which is more in tune with being playful.

If you have the space in the room for cabinets or drawers which can be reserved for each child you see, they can put their special items in it (i.e. drawings, secrets). This can often enhance their attachment to the room. If this is used, other children must not have access to these "personal spaces".

The room should by kept neat and orderly. I expect each child (and me) to clean up the room prior to the end of each session. Try to check the room a few minutes prior to each session to make sure all is in order and, if not, do so. This is probably a sore spot in my practice as other therapists sometimes do not have this expectation and I have come into a room with toys strewn all over, or all the chalk or paint is used up, or all the checkers are not together. Mutual respect and consideration makes life so much easier. However, life being as it is, you need to be prepared to take care of your part in order to gain the full potential of your work.

To reiterate, you do not need to have a fancy play therapy room with all the newest toys to be a good play therapist. I have worked in rooms not much larger than a closet and in school gymnasiums. A part of the challenge is being able to adapt to the environment when necessary and not to let the environment have control over you.

References

Andolfi, M.   *Behind the Family Mask: Therapeutic Change in Rigid Family Systems,* (New York), Brunner/Mazel, 1983.

Axline, V.   *Play Therapy,* (Boston), Houghton Mifflin Company, 1947.

Bowen, Murray   "Bowen on Triangles", March 1974, Workshop transcribed by Ken Terkelsen.

Caplan, F. & T.   *The Power of Play,* (New York), Anchor Press/Doubleday, 1965.

Fogarty, T.   "Triangles", *The Family,* Vol 2, number 2, 1975. p 11-21.

Fox, E.. Nelson, M., Bolman, W.   "The Termination Process: A Neglected Dimension in Social Work", *Social Work,* October 1969.

Framo, J.   *Exploration in Marital and Family Therapy,* (New York), Springer Publishing Company, 1982.

Freud, Anna   *Normality and Pathology in Childhood: The Writings of Anna Freud, Vol. 6,* (New York), International Universities Press, 1965.

Gardiner, R.   *Psychotherapeutic Approaches to the Resistant Child,* (New York), Jason Aronson, 1975.

Haley, Jay   *Changing Families,* (New York), Gruhne & Stratton, 1971.

Haworth, Mary   *Child Psychotherapy,* (New York), Basic Books, 1964.

Koman, Stuart Stechler, G.   *Making the Jump to Systems,* The Handbook of Adolescent and Family Therapy, Edited by M.P. Mirkin and Stuart L. Koman, Gardner Press, (New York), 1985.

Mahler, M.   *The Psychological Birth of the Human Infant,* (New York), Basic Books, 1975.

Millar, Suzanna   *The Psychology of Play,* (London), Penguin Books, 1977.

Mills, J. Crowley, R.   *Therapeutic Metaphors for Children and the Child Within,* (New York), Brunner/Mazel Publishers, 1986.

Neubauer, P.(ed.)	*The Process of Child Development*, (New York), Meridian, 1976.
Papp, Peggy	*The Process of Change*, (New York), Guilford Press, 1983.
Piaget, Jean	*The Psychology of the Child*, (New York), Routledge and Kegan Paul, 1969.
Pickard, P.M.	*The Activity of Children*, (New York), The Humanities Press, 1967.
Rychlak, Joseph	*Introduction to Personality and Psychotherapy*, (Boston), Houghton Mifflin, 1973.
Samuels, S. (Ed)	*Enhancing Self-Concept in Early Childhood*, (New York), Human Sciences Press, 1977.
Sarason, Irwin	*Abnormal Psychology*, (New York), Appleton, Century, Crofts, 1972.
Snyder, N. R.& R.	*The Young Child as a Person*, (New York), Human Sciences Press, 1980.
Klein, Melanie	*The Psychoanalysis of Children*, (New York) Delacorte Press/Seymour Lawrence, 1975.

Bibliography

CHAPTER 1

The Importance Of Play

Axline, V.   *Play Therapy,* (Boston), Houghton Mifflin Company, 1947.

Caplan, F. & T.   *The Power of Play,* (New York), Anchor Press/ Doubleday, 1965.

Millar, S.   *The Psychology of Play,* (London) Penguin Books, 1977.

Samuels, S. (Ed)   *Enhancing Self-Concept in Early Childhood,* (New York), Human Sciences Press, 1977.

Snyder, N. R. & R.   *The Young Child as Person,* (New York), Human Sciences Press, 1980.

CHAPTER 2

Child Development

Almy, M. (ed.)   *Early Childhood Play,* (New York), Selected Academic Readings, 1968.

Ansbacker, H Ansbacker, R. (eds.)   *The Individual Psychology of Alfred Adler,* (New York), Basic Book Inc., 1956

Arnold, A.   *Teaching Your Child to Learn,* (New York), Prentice-Hall, 1971.

Biggar, J.   *Psychotherapy and Child Development, an Introduction for Students,* (London), Tavistock Publication, 1966.

Erikson, Erik   *Childhood and Society,* (New York), W.W. Norton & Company Inc., 1950.

Freud, Anna   *Normality and Pathology in Childhood: The Writings of Anna Freud, Vol. 6,* (New York), International Universities Press, 1965.

Fraiberg, Selma   *The Magic Years*, (New York), Charles Scribner's Sons, 195

Frank, Lawrence   "The Role of Play in Child Development", *Childhood Education*, (45), 1968. p 149-152.

Klein, Melanie   *The Psychoanalysis of Children*, (New York), Delacorte Press/Seymour Lawrence, 1975.

Mahler, M.   *The Psychological Birth of the Human Infant*, (New York), Basic Books, 1975.

Millar, Suzanna   *The Psychology of Play*, (London), Penguin Books, 1977.

Neubauer, P.(ed.)   *The Process of Child Development*, (New York), Meridian, 1976.

Piaget, Jean   *The Psychology of the Child*, (New York), Routledge and Kegan Paul, 1969.

Pickard, P.M.   *The Activity of Children*, (New York), The Humanities Press, 1967.

Samuels, Shirley   *Enhancing Self-concept in Early Childhood*, (New York), Human Sciences Press, 1977.

Scarr, S.   *Understanding Development*, (Toronto), Harcourt Brace
Weinberg, R.   Jovanovich Publishers, 1986.
Levine, A.

Snyder, N. R.& R.   *The Young Child as a Person*, (New York), Human Sciences Press, 1980.

CHAPTER 3

Child Management And Parenting

Coloroso, B.   *Winning at Parenting...Kids Are Worth It*, (U.S.A.), 1989.

Dreikurs, R.   *Coping with Children's Misbehaviour*, (New York), Hawthorn Press, 1972.

Dreikurs, R.   *Discipline Without Tears*, (New York), Dutton, 1974.

Haley, Jay   *Leaving Home*, (New York), McGraw-Hill, 1980.

Kaye, Kenneth   *Family Rules: Raising Responsible Children*, (New York), Walker and Company, 1984.

Visher, E.& J.   *Stepfamilies: A Guide to Working with Stepfamilies and Step Children*, (New York), Brunner/Mazel, 1979.

CHAPTER 4

Systems

Ackerman, N.	"Adolescent Problems: A Symptom of Family Disorder", *Family Process*, 1962. p 202.
Andolfi, M.	*Behind the Family Mask: Therapeutic Change in Rigid Family Systems*, (New York), Brunner/Mazel, 1983.
Bertalanffy, L.	"General System Theory", *General Systems Yearbook*, (1), 1956. p 1-10.
Framo, J.	*Exploration in Marital and Family Therapy*, (New York), Springer Publishing Company, 1982.
Haley, Jay	*Changing Families*, (New York), Gruhne & Stratton, 1971.
Koman, Stuart Stechler, G.	*Making the Jump to Systems,* The Handbook of Adolescent and Family Therapy, Edited by M.P. Mirkin and Stuart L. Koman, Gardner Press, (New York), 1985.
Nichols, M.	*The Self in the System*, (New York), Brunner/Mazel Publishers, 1987.
Noone, Robert	"Symbiosis, the Family and Natural Systems", *Family Process*, 27(3), September 1988. p 285-292.
Papp, Peggy	*The Process of Change* (New York), The Guilford Press, 1983.

CHAPTER 5

Triangulation

Bowen, Murray	*Family Therapy In Clinical Practice*, (New York), Jason Aronson Inc., 1978.
Bowen, Murray	"Bowen on Triangles", March 1974, Workshop transcribed by Ken Terkelsen.
Minuchin, S.	*Families and Family Therapy*, (Cambridge), Harvard University Press, 1974.
Fogarty, T.	"Triangles", *The Family*, Vol 2, number 2, 1975. p 11-21.

CHAPTER 6

Transference/Counter-transference

Gardiner, R.　　*Psychotherapeutic Approaches to the Resistant Child*, (New York), Jason Aronson, 1975.

Haworth, Mary　*Child Psychotherapy*, (New York), Basic Books, 1964.

Rychlak, Joseph　*Introduction to Personality and Psychotherapy*, (Boston), Houghton Mifflin, 1973.

Sarason, Irwin　*Abnormal Psychology*, (New York), Appleton, Century, Crofts, 1972.

Taffel, Ron　"In Praise of Counter-Transference", *The Family Therapy Networker*, Jan/Feb. 1993. p 52-57.

CHAPTER 7

Hypothesis-building

Cecchin, G.　"Hypothesizing, Circularity and Neutrality Revisited: An Invitation to Curiosity", *Family Process*, 26(4), December 1987. p 405-413.

Keeney, B.P.　*Aesthetics of Change*, (New York), Guilford Press, 1978.

Papp, Peggy　*The Process of Change*, (New York), Guilford Press, 1983.

Sadler, John　"Hypothesizing and Evidence-Gathering: The Nexus of
Hulgus, Yosaf　Understanding", *Family Process*, 28(3), Sept. 1989. p 255-26

Tomm, K.　"Interventive Interviewing: Part I, Strategizing as a Fourth Guideline for the Therapist", *Family Process*, 26: 3-13, 1987.

CHAPTER 8

Termination

Barnes, Mark	"Endings", *Playground*, Winter 1991. p 8.
Fox, E. Nelson, M., Bolman, W.	"The Termination Process: A Neglected Dimension in Social Work", *Social Work*, October 1969.
Ross, Allen	"Interruptions and Termination of Treatment", *Child Psychotherapy*, (New York), Basic Books, 1964. p 290-292.
Schiff, Sheldon	"Termination of Therapy: Problems in a Community Psychiatric Outpatient Clinic", *Archives of General Psychology*, 6(1), January 1962. p 77-82.

CHAPTER 9

Techniques

Adler, Margot	*Drawing Down the Moon*, (Boston), Beacon Press, 1981.
Bettelheim, B.	*The Uses of Enchantment: The Meaning and Importance of Fairy Tales*, (New York), Vintage, 1979.
Bowyen, Ruth	*The Lowenfeld World Techniques,* (Oxford), Pergamon Press, 1970.
Davis, Nancy	"The Use of Therapeutic Stories in the Treatment of Abused Children", *Journal of Strategic and Systemic Therapies,* Vol 8, number 4, Winter, 1989.
Duphouse, J. W.	"Music Therapy: A Valuable Adjunct to Psychotherapy with Children", *Psychiatric Quarterly Supplement,* 42(1), 1968. p 75-78.
Gardiner, R.	"Dramatized Story-telling in Child Psychotherapy", *Acta Paedopsychiatrica*, 41(5), 1975. p 110-116.
Gardiner, R.	*Psychotherapeutic Approaches to the Resistant Child*, (New York) Jason Aronson, 1975.
Ginott, H. G.	*Group Psychotherapy with Children* (New York) Doubleday & Company Inc., 1954.
Gondor, E. I.	*Art and Play Therapy*, (New York), Doubleday & Company Inc., 1954.

Heemlich, E. P.	"Paraverbal Techniques in the Therapy of Childhood Communication Disorders", *International Journal of Child Psychotherapy*, 1(1), Jan. 1972. p 65-83.
Hill, Gareth	*Sandplay Studies*, (San Francisco), C.G. Jung, 1981.
Irwin, E.	"Family Puppet Interview", *Family Process*, 14, 1975. p 179-191.
Kalff, Dora	*Sandplay: A Psychotherapeutic Approach to the Psyche*, (Santa Monica), Sigo Press, 1980.
Kelley, C	"Play Desensitization of Fear of Darkness in Preschool Children", *Dissertation Abstract*, 35 (1-B), July 1974. p 510
Kritzberg, N.	*The Structured Therapeutic Game Method of Child Analytic Psychotherapy*, (New York), Exposition Press, 1975.
Lankton, C & S.	*Tales of Enchantment: Goal-Oriented Metaphors for Adults and Children in Therapy*, (New York), Brunner/Mazel Publishers, 1989.
Lockwood, J.	"Psychodrama: A Therapeutic Tool with Children in Group Play Therapy", *Group Psychotherapy & Psychodrama*, 26(3-4), 1973. p 53-67.
Loomis, E.	"The Use of Checkers in Handling Certain Resistances in Child Therapy", *Journal of American Psychoanalytic Association*, (5), 1957. p 130-135.
Lubimiv, G.	"Getting Unstuck In Play Therapy", *Playground*, Winter 1991. p 3-4.
Lubimiv, G.	"Good Game - The Clinical Use of Checkers", *Playground*, Spring 1993. p 6-7.
Maclay, David	*Treatment for Children*, (London), George Allen & Unwin Ltd., 1970.
Mills, J. Crowley, R.	*Therapeutic Metaphors for Children and the Child Within*, (New York), Brunner/Mazel Publishers, 1986.
Moore, Robin	*Awakening the Hidden Storyteller: How to Build a Storytelling Tradition in Your Family*, (Boston), Shambhala, 1991.
Moskowitz, J.	"The Sorcerer's Apprentice or the Use of Magic in Child Psychotherapy", *International Journal of Psychotherapy*, 2(2), April 1973. p 138-162.
Naumberg, M.	*An Introduction to Art Therapy*, (New York), Teachers College Press, 1973.

Oaklander, V.   *Windows to our Children*, (New York), Real People Press, 1969.

Robertson, M.   "Shadow Therapy with Children", *American Journal of Psychotherapy*, 23(3), 1969. p 505-509.

Schaefer, C.   *Innovative Interventions in Child and Adolescent Therapy*, (New York), Wiley, 1988.

Takacs, Viki   "Talking With Rocks", *Playground*, Spring 1983. p 5-6.

Weinrib, E.   *Images of Self: The Sandplay Therapy Process*, (Boston) Sigo Press, 1983.

Additional Reading Suggestions

THEORY

Ellis, M.J.	*Why People Play*, (Englewood Cliffs, N.J.), Prentice-Hall, 1973.
Erikson, Erik	*Childhood and Society*, (New York), W. W. Norton, 1950.
Freud, Anna	*Normality and Pathology in Childhood: The Writings of Anna Freud, Vol. 6*, (New York), International Universities Press, 1965.
Lewis, Jerry	"Childhood Play in Normality, Pathology and Therapy", *American Journal of Orthopsychiatry*, 63(1), January 1993. p 6-15.
Mahler, M.	*The Psychological Birth of the Human Infant*, (New York), Basic Books, 1975.
McNabb, O.	"A Compilation of Selected Rationale and Research in Play Therapy", *Dissertation Abstracts International*, 36 (5-A), November 1975. p 2637.
Mook, Bertha	"Play in Child Psychotherapy", *The Social Work Practitioner*, September 1988. p 42-47.
Moustakas, C.	*Children in Play Therapy*, (New York), Ballantine, 1974.
Ornstein, Anna	"Making Contact with the Inner World of the Child: Towards a Theory of Psychoanalytic Psychotherapy with Children", *Comprehensive Psychiatry*, 17(1), Jan-Feb 1976. p 3-36.
Piaget, Jean	*The Psychology of the Child*, (New York), Routledge and Kegan Paul, 1969.
Reisman, J. M.	*Principles of Psychotherapy with Children*, (Toronto), John Wiley & Sons, 1973.
Schaefer, C.	*The Therapeutic Use of Child's Play*, (New York), Jason Aronson, 1976.
Yawkey, T. D.	*Child's Play and Play Therapy*, (Lancaster), Technomic, 1984.

MODELS

Axline, V.	*Play Therapy*, (Boston), Houghton Mifflin Company, 1944.
Fakouri, M. E.	"Some Clinical Implications of Piaget's Theory", *Psychology* 13(1), Feb. 1976. p 33-36.
Ginott, H. G.	*Group Psychotherapy with Children*, (Toronto), McGraw-Hill, 1961.
Graham, Bill	"Non-directive Play Therapy with Troubled Children", *Corrective & Social Psychiatry & Journal of Behavioral Technology Methods and Therapy*, 21(1), 1975. p 21-23.
Haworth, M.	*Child Psychotherapy: Practice & Theory*, (New York), Basic Books, 1964.
Jernberg, Ann	*Theraplay*, (San Francisco), Joey-Bass, 1980.
Moustakas, C.	*Existential Child Therapy*, (New York), Basic Books, 1966.
Schaefer, C. E.	*Therapies for Children*, (San Francisco), Joey-Bass, 1977.

CREATIVE THINKING

Aaron, David	*Child's Play*, (New York), Harper and Row, 1965.
Caplan, F. & T.	*The Power of Play*, (New York), Anchor Press/Doubleday, 1973.
De Bono, Edward	*Lateral Thinking*, (London), Penguin Books, 1990.
De Bono, Edward	*de Bono's Thinking Course*, (New York), Facts On File Inc., 1985.
Edwards, Betty	*Drawing From the Right Side of the Brain*, (Los Angeles), Jeremy P. Tarcher Inc., 1989.
Pickard, P. M.	*The Activity of Children*, (New York), The Humanities Press, 1967.

About the Author

A native of Winnipeg, Manitoba, Gregory Paul Lubimiv holds a Bachelor of Social Work from Laurentian University and a Masters of Social Work from the University of Toronto. He has worked as a social worker in the North-West Territories, a child welfare worker in Northern Ontario and, since 1977, he has been the Executive Director of a children's mental health clinic in Eastern Ontario.

In 1988, Mr. Lubimiv obtained certification as a Child and Play Therapist and Play Therapist Supervisor from the Canadian Association of Child and Play Therapy. Being the third eldest of ten children and the father of five children have also enriched his experience with family life and play.

Mr. Lubimiv also operates Transitions, a private practice, which provides a wide range of consultation, training and evaluation services in relation to mental health, organizational and community issues.